"Is this wise?"

Because her mind was on sensation and nothing else, it was a moment before Lory acknowledged that something was being asked of her. Why wasn't it possible to continue to float in this wonderful world Mike was creating for her? "I'm not going to fall asleep if that's what you're talking about," she said at last.

His lips were on her neck. Pinpricks of heat chased one another down her body and welled up inside her. She was a tinder-dry forest being touched by fire.

"I didn't think you were. It's going to be a long time before I can fall asleep tonight, Lory. That's the kind of impact you're having on me. We're playing with fire."

Dear Reader:

We at Silhouette are very excited to bring you a NEW reading **Sensation**. *Look out for the four books which will appear in our new Silhouette* **Sensation** *series every month. These stories will have the high quality you have come to expect from Silhouette, and their varied and provocative plots will encourage you to explore the wonder of falling in love – again and again!*

Emotions run high in these drama-filled novels. Greater sensual detail and an extra edge of realism intensify the hero and heroine's relationship so that you cannot help but be caught up in their every change of mood.

We hope you enjoy this new **Sensation** *– and will go on to enjoy many more.*

We would love to hear your comments about our new line and encourage you to write to us:

Jane Nicholls
Silhouette Books
PO Box 236
Thornton Road
Croydon
Surrey
CR9 3RU

VELLA MUNN
Firedance

*First published in Great Britain in 1989
by Silhouette Books, Eton House, 18–24 Paradise Road,
Richmond, Surrey TW9 1SR*

© Vella Munn 1988

Silhouette, Silhouette Sensation and Colophon are
Trade Marks of Harlequin Enterprises B.V.

ISBN 0 373 57667 8

18–8909

Made and printed in Great Britain

Chapter One

Lory Foster had forgotten what the sky looked like, or what it was like to hear anything but the crack and angry screams of a molten monster. With her back bowed and her hands wrapped around the handle of her shovel, she felt too much like a lion tamer thrust into a cage filled with wild beasts.

A lion tamer had the easier job. At least the creatures he faced had a single form. They weren't constantly shifting and changing, taking over the only world Lory knew, making her forget there'd ever been anything else but this insanity. Corralling a forest fire was like trying to chain the wind.

She wasn't going to think about that. She was going to do what she'd been brought here for. "A shower," Lory said, sighing. The sound was lost in the crackle of flames. "I'd give three days of overtime pay for a shower," she repeated because she needed to hear her voice.

"You can have your shower. First thing I want is an ice-cream sundae. Five scoops. One vanilla and four chocolate. Don't spare the whip cream."

"You don't ever change, do you, Boyd?" As she spoke, her shovel made another of the endless assaults on the dry grass underfoot. She dug down to roots and flipped her load over to expose bare earth. *Try to eat that,* she told the approaching flames. *I hope you starve.* "Always thinking of your stomach," she teased the sweating fire fighter next to her. "I just hope I can stay awake long enough for that shower. I swear I could sleep propped against a tree." Another shovelful of dirt went sunny-side up. Lory could only shrug in silent apology to the wiggling earthworm she'd dislodged. It wasn't as if any of them had a choice. The forest was in the grip of a madman. Sacrifices had to be made if any of them were going to survive.

"Stay awake," Boyd warned. "Damn it's hot. Listen to that monster. The wind's really whipping it."

"It's getting closer." Lory didn't bother with a telling look in Boyd's direction. There was only the pull and release, pull and release in her shoulders. That and listening. She hated it when the wind kicked up. "We should be fishing. I've seen more worms today—"

"What we should be doing is hightailing it out of here. Why do these lightning strikes always happen where it's too steep for any machinery?"

"Murphy's Law?" Lory suggested. "My calves are killing me. If I have to climb another hill—"

Alerted by a sound at odds with their surroundings, Lory cocked her head. A moment later the smoke thinned. She located the source of the high-pitched whine. "What's that?" She pointed skyward. Her other hand held her hard hat in place. Sweat trickled down her back. "Would you look at that. That's got to be the biggest chopper I've ever seen."

Boyd Doughtery leaned against his own round-pointed shovel and stared through smoke and trees at the whirling blades overhead. Under the hovering helicopter they could make out a heavily laden bag sling that blocked out any glimpse of whoever was piloting the massive machine. "You're telling me," he said, whistling. "It's sure not one of ours. We don't have anything half that big."

A moment later the helicopter passed out of view. Almost before the sounds of crackling pitch swallowed that of the powerful engine, Lory dismissed its presence. She lowered her head, once again focusing on the fingers of fire that snaked through the forest like relentless creatures from a horror movie. She had only one goal: expose earth and give the fire nothing to fuel itself.

Fascinating as the massive helicopter was, there wasn't time to see where the pilot intended to drop his load. A foehn wind had formed in the mountain range to the west, dropping the humidity to no more than five percent. For three days Lory and the rest of the hotshot crew had been praying that the wind wouldn't climb above forty miles per hour. As long as they stayed out of the wind's path, the fire fighters were relatively safe, but they were running out of luck. The word from the crew boss an hour ago was that the hot, dry wind was picking up speed. Unless something happened, and fast, controlling the fire would be out of the question.

Sucking in air almost warm enough to singe her eyelashes, Lory changed tactics. Now she started digging into the soft earth and throwing dirt at the nearest flames. If she couldn't starve the damn fire, she could try to smother it. Before she could pick up another load, the newcomer overhead was back again. The hissing roar caused by the monster helicopter washed over the crackle of burning pine needles. The chopper dipped lower, risking a death dance with flames that shot forty feet into the air.

"Don't do anything stupid," Lory whispered hoarsely. "Don't be a hero. We don't want to have to bail you out." Despite the grinding need that had kept her on the fire line for three days except for brief rest periods, Lory glanced upward again. Light from the burnt orange sun reflected off metal and sent sparks of light back into the sky.

The pilot was so free! She was stuck here on the ground fighting the results of a summer storm while he had the means at hand to leave behind this man-made inferno. Fantasy took over. The chopper would dump its load, but instead of veering back to the river to replenish itself, the empty bag would be dropped lower and lower until Lory could climb aboard. She'd be asleep before they cleared the treetops.

Crew chief Keith Hartigan effectively put an end to the dream. The solid, long-legged man was beside her almost before Lory saw him coming. "Did you see that?" He, too, pointed skyward. "That man just might be our salvation. I'll tell you, being out here where we can't get any ground equipment in to help us has really put us at a disadvantage. We had our backs against it before he showed up. Now— maybe—we'd be out of a job if we had more of those."

"Where'd he come from?" Lory wiped sweat from her forehead, not because she had anything to hide from the crew chief, but because dirt and grime and exhaustion were getting the best of her. Lory might be in great physical shape, but she was human. She hadn't been joking when she'd told Boyd she'd give any amount of money for a shower. "He isn't one of ours."

Keith held up the walkie-talkie that kept him in touch with fire headquarters. "Nope. The guy's an independent. Where he came from, I have no idea, but he's saving our bacon." Keith grunted and wiped sweat off his own forehead. "I'd say he's carrying a good four hundred gallons in that bag."

Lory whistled. That was four times the amount of water most helicopters could handle. She opened her mouth, but before she could speak, the chopper once again passed overhead heading toward the fire's front line. As Lory watched what she could see of the chopper through the trees, the pilot expertly released his load, sending a red cascade of fire retardant into the forest. Almost before the retardant hit the ground, the chopper spun around and headed back the way it had come. "He's fighting a hell of a wind. I hope he has the power."

"He does. How are you doing? You getting enough water?"

Lory nodded. Three years ago she would have resented being asked such a question, but three years ago she was green. Now as a seasoned fire fighter, she knew that adrenaline exhaustion and the plodding pressure of fire fighting could make a person forget a simple but essential thing like not getting dehydrated. "I'm doing fine, but you better talk to Boyd. He's got this incredible ice-cream fix. He'll flounder on the stuff if we don't keep an eye on him."

Chuckling, Keith patted Lory on the shoulder before turning to leave. "We've got reporters back at camp. They want to talk to you when you come in."

"Me? Keith, you know I don't want to talk to those guys. If you've set me up—"

"Not me. Someone told them there were two women in the hotshot crew. You know, human interest."

"So let them talk to Ann."

Keith's eyes rolled skyward. "No, thank you. At least *you* won't burn their ears. It's a good thing she's married to a trucker. No one else would put up with that language. Tell them something so they'll leave. I don't much give a damn what."

Lory didn't try to keep Keith after that. The crew chief had a point about her being a better spokesperson. Ann Larsen had an instinct about the nature of forest fires that Lory would give anything to duplicate, but the older woman certainly didn't pull any punches. True, Lory swore on the fire line, especially if the fire was the result of human stupidity, and what she yelled when smoke jumping would shock anyone except another smoke jumper, but at least Lory knew enough to leave certain words behind once a fire was out. She could tell the reporters about the methods that were being used to fight this particular fire and then direct them to someone else for information about how many acres had been burned.

Still, she'd had more than one interview with reporters more interested in why a slightly built young woman with big dark eyes and waves of auburn hair was fighting fires than the story of the fire itself. If she had to dodge one more question about her marital status or why a sweet young thing would want to be out on the line—

"I'm timing him," Boyd called out as Lory went back to the tedious and dangerous task of clearing the forest floor down to bare earth ahead of the fingers of flame. "He's making a drop just about every three minutes. That guy's working as hard as we are."

"And probably getting paid twice as much," Lory yelled back as the chopper once again came into view. "That really is something. I wonder how he's able to mix retardant into the water while he's flying."

"Why don't you ask him?"

Fat chance, Lory thought. Whoever he was, the pilot would probably take off the minute the fire was out. Surely he had better things to do than wander into camp to chew the fat with the ground crew. Besides, raw as Lory's throat felt, she wouldn't be able to let out more than a squeak around either him or the unwanted reporters.

For the next two hours Lory existed as nothing more than a fire-fighting machine. Keith was right. If they were going by the textbook, there would be bulldozers here to do much of the muscle work, but the terrain was too steep. Lory and her fellow fire fighters and the lightweight shovels they carried were the lone defense against the fire. Either they cut off the monster's vicious appetite or they might as well pack it in. Might as well leave the forest to face an ugly death, Lory amended. Well, she wasn't going to let that happen. As long as there was strength in her shoulders and arms, she would dig and expose, dig and throw.

To the creatures fleeing the monster it must have felt as if the world had gone insane, but as fires went this one kept the adrenaline charge somewhere in the medium range for Lory. When the crews had first gone out to the fire, they'd had hopes of bringing it under control without much difficulty, but that was before the wind had kicked up. What made putting the fire out doubly complicated was the wind's unpredictable nature.

For most of the morning the wind had been coming in from the west, but shortly after noon it had shifted to the north, which had forced the crews to scramble around to the new front. The forest service's water tankers had been hampered by the steep terrain and the twenty miles they had to travel to refill. And, to make matters worse, three of the district's tanker planes were already in service fighting another fire. So if it hadn't been for the relentless work of the massive helicopter dumping load after load at the fire's forward edge, containment would have been impossible.

Now, however, as day faded into dusk and the fickle wind settled down, Lory was able to see the beginning of the end. Soon the night crew would be taking over and she could begin the task of responding to her body's demands—and, if possible, thanking the pilot responsible for turning a frantic scramble into a routine mop-up procedure.

Twice, when the crew chief was nearby, she heard the pilot's voice over the walkie-talkie. He impressed her as a no-nonsense man who'd been doing this work long enough that he'd picked up an instinct about a fire's nature. "You let me worry about that," he'd said once in response to something someone at headquarters had said. "I know how low to go with this baby."

"Independent cuss, isn't he?" Lory had observed at the time, but it wasn't until she and the rest of the crew were trudging over to the van that would take them to the luxury of food and a shower that she gave his terse statement a second thought. If there was one thing Lory had learned about fire fighting, it was that caring about those she worked side by side with was as natural as wearing a hard hat. Someone who resented words of advice and concern belonged alone in his private flying world.

Lory accepted the helping hand that boosted her into the ash-coated van and sank into a seat next to Ann Larsen. The other woman spoke without opening her eyes. "Damn, I'm getting too old to do this. Why didn't I turn out to be a hairdresser like my mother wanted?"

Lory sighed and let her head flop back against warm plastic. Her feet felt swollen in her high boots, but she was too tired to reach for the laces. She tried to focus on her hands, but keeping her eyelids open was too much of an effort. "Admit it, Ann. We've got to be crazy to do this."

"I'm not going to argue that. But what about doing it because of the male/female ratio? There's enough men here to make any woman happy. We could have our own harem."

Lory didn't bother to pick up her end of the long-standing mock argument she and Ann had about eligible men in their line of work. Even if Ann weren't married, Lory couldn't see her co-worker setting her sights on any of the dirty, exhausted men sharing the van with them. Ann was self-contained. Independent. A husband, Ann declared, was handy for filling out income tax forms, keeping her car running and keeping her bed warm at night. Other than that Ann wasn't very clear on why she'd been married for ten years.

Her opinion on what Lory should be doing about the excess of men was another story. According to Ann, Lory was a fool for treating the other fire fighters like brothers. "You can't be blind," she'd told Lory more than once. "You gotta know the way they ogle your rump. Why the hell do you think all the bachelors want to work next to you?''

Lory was halfway through forming a mental rebuttal when she fell asleep. Despite the bouncing journey to the command post, Lory was oblivious to the world until the van jerked to a stop. "Rise and shine, children," the driver called out. "Looks like we get to smile for the camera."

In the growing dusk Lory could see a station wagon bearing the call letters of a local TV station. She didn't bother to stifle a groan. Beyond the wagon was the small-town school gym with the promised shower that had kept her sane all afternoon. She could catch the scent of dinner coming from the school's cafeteria, a scent stirred up by the slowly rotating blades of the helicopter resting on the football field.

MIKE STEEN JUMPED DOWN out of his seat but didn't immediately head for the knots of people around the vehicles and buildings. Leery of the questions he knew would be thrown at him, he put off the moment when he would have to submit himself to reporters. But it was too dark to make any more drops, and Mike's throat was dry. His stomach refused to be ignored. He would get something to eat, maybe grab a few hours of sleep and then make a call to see if his services were needed elsewhere.

One of the day crews was just getting out of their van, ten hot, dusty, exhausted men pushing aching legs one step at a time. Mike sympathized with those who fought fire with muscle and sweat, but because his work kept him in the air he knew little about what motivated those on the ground. Sometimes he wondered if he knew what motivated anyone, even himself. Not that he gave it a lot of thought. Flying. Watching the world from somewhere just above it suited him well.

Mike's hand stopped halfway on its journey to the back of his neck where a knotted muscle demanded attention. He was wrong. Two of the men were women. The first to clump out of the van was built along the lines of a farm wife with broad hips and back, solid legs, and tangled hair escaping from whatever was holding it close to her neck.

The other one was a different story. Despite her mustard-colored fire shirt, Mike could make out the clean, spare lines of a healthy young woman. She had caught up with a couple of the men and was walking between them as if trying to shield herself from the approaching reporter. *It isn't going to work, lady,* Mike told her silently. The reporter would have to be blind not to notice the mass of hair she was lifting from her scalp, or the mind-riveting way her tired old jeans were doing all the right things.

Much more interested in his surroundings than he'd been a couple of minutes ago, Mike closed the chopper door and started for the center of activity. The community school had been turned into a makeshift command post complete with pumper trucks, spare tools, and a camper holding the equipment needed for communication. Workers just off the fire line were heading toward the cafeteria while others were getting in line for the showers. He watched the two women shoot the men a superior look before starting toward the empty girls' half of the gym. They almost made it.

"Just a minute please," Mike heard the reporter say. "Are you Ms. Foster?"

"Yes," came a weary, wary reply that registered somewhere deep inside Mike and made walking toward strangers worth the effort.

"I'd like to talk to you if you don't mind." The reporter's tone indicated that whether the tired fire fighter minded or not was of no concern to him. "I'm looking for a human interest angle. I understand you've been fighting fires for three summers."

"Yes," the woman repeated. She offered nothing more.

"What do you weigh?"

"What did you ask?" Lory squared around to face the obstacle that stood between her and a shower. Life flashed in her big dark eyes. "What kind of story is this?"

"I'm just curious as to why an attractive young woman would be out here fighting fires when she could be home powdering her nose."

"Is that what women do when they're home?" Lory taunted. "Mister, I'm really not the one you should be talking to. There's my crew boss or someone from the command center. What about the pilot of that big chopper? If it hadn't been for him, we wouldn't have this fire under control."

"Yeah. What about me? Don't I rate a line in this paper of yours?" demanded Mike, a man who never before in his life had sought publicity. As the woman shot him a look of gratitude, he knew why he'd opened his mouth. He could handle the press. She'd been through enough today. "Why don't you let her go get cleaned up while we talk?" he offered. "Your fire fighter looks out on her feet."

"Would you mind?" Lory asked the reporter. Her arms were hanging heavily at her sides. Although her shovel was in the van, her hands felt welded to it. She tried to nod at the big rawboned man with the squared-off face, and eyes that said he knew what she was feeling but lacked the energy to tell her. "I'll answer your questions in a few minutes. I promise."

The reporter looked doubtful. "I have a deadline."

Mike pointed at his helicopter. "I think you've got more than ample material for a story there. That's a Sikorsky SF58E I'm flying. It carries 420 gallons of water in that bag, about four times more than most choppers. I have it rigged so I can mix retardant in with the water while I'm in the air. Is there anything else you need to know? Do you have enough flash for a picture?" Mike placed himself strategically between the woman and the reporter. The sound of her quickly retreating footsteps told him that she'd taken advantage of the diversion he'd created.

For the next ten minutes Mike took the reporter on a tour of his helicopter and answered questions about the life of an independent contractor doing business with forest firefighting agencies. He didn't have to concentrate on what he was saying, so his mind was free to mentally follow Ms. Foster into the high school shower. Since it was the middle of summer, he wasn't sure whether the hot water had been turned on. Would goose bumps break out on her smooth flesh? Would she take time to shampoo dust and smoke from her shoulder-length hair? She'd been carrying a backpack. Did she have clean civilian clothes to change into, tennis shoes instead of the sturdy boots worn on the fire line?

"It started out with a simple turbine engine. I've souped it up so that it now carries about a thousand more pounds than it did originally," Mike was explaining as the gym door opened again. Whatever he was about to say died.

Superb. Absolutely exquisite. Ms. Foster was still wearing jeans, although this pair was clean and hung as if her legs had been made for clinging denim. Tennis shoes now covered her feet. She had on a sleeveless tank top that did nothing to hide the fact that her breasts were full and her bra not quite equal to the job. Her shoulders slumped forward tiredly.

She'd shampooed her hair. Although damp tendrils still lay across her bare shoulders, the bulk had been fluffed up off her forehead. He didn't think she was wearing makeup, but in the dark he couldn't tell whether the definition came from artificial means or was due to natural shadows around her deep-set eyes. Gloss, probably to treat chapped lips, glistened under the school's parking lot lights.

Mike smiled, aware of the common threads that ran between him and this woman. Without pretense or question or explanation she was who she was. It was the way he lived his life.

"Are you feeling human?" he asked softly when she was close enough.

So she hadn't imagined it. All the time the tepid water was slapping life back into her, Lory had been thinking about one man who'd stood out from the others. It wasn't anything she could put a finger on, any mannerism or look. It was simply that the helicopter pilot's eyes met hers head-on and stayed where they belonged unlike the wandering eyes of the reporter. His mouth was firm, almost hard, and yet there was nothing to shy away from in that hardness. He was large enough to control the monster he'd spent the day in. Still, he wasn't using his size to dominate the situation, and she admired him for that. She couldn't tell much about his complexion in the poor lighting but guessed that it had been fashioned by wind and heat. The neck of his T-shirt was losing its grip on the rest of the fabric and his jeans had seen even more service than hers, but his boots were the best money could buy.

"I don't know if I've gotten to the point of feeling human yet," Lory remembered to say. "But I feel much better than I did a few minutes ago."

"Hungry?"

Hunger was a sensation that had yet to make an impact, but she was thirsty. "Maybe later." Lory licked her lips.

"How about a beer?" The chopper pilot nodded at his machine. "I have a few on ice in there."

Being offered a beer by a stranger didn't faze Lory. A fire had brought them together. That cut past the social amenities that usually had to be adhered to. "Thanks, but no," she replied. "When I'm this thirsty only water will do. Lots of it."

"Then water it is. I have that, too. Ice-cold."

Lory's eyes widened as she again licked her lips. At the moment she would sell one of her brothers for a glass of water. "You've just made an offer I can't refuse." She turned toward the chopper and took a step but then faltered. "How far is it over there? I'm not sure I can make it."

The reporter spoke up. "Why don't you go get the water, Mike? That'll give me time to ask Ms. Foster a couple of questions."

"Do you have to?" Lory asked. "I don't know that much about the whole picture."

"I already have that information," the reporter insisted. "What I want to do is single you out for the human-interest angle. You'd like your name in the paper, wouldn't you?"

Turning so the reporter couldn't see, Lory lifted her eyes skyward for Mike's sake. "Not particularly, but fire away." *Mike. A simple, uncomplicated, sturdy name. Did it fit?*

Without ceremony Lory bent her legs under her and settled heavily onto the grassy area near the flagpole. Getting the interview over with, like going to the dentist, was better not delayed. "This is probably a mistake," she said as her head sagged forward. "I may never get up again."

The man known as Mike was disappearing into the darkness. Lory kept her eyes on where he'd been standing, not on the slacks-clad man with the roving eyes settling down next to her. It wasn't until the reporter tapped her knee with his pencil that she pulled herself back to what had to be done.

"That's a fascinating job Mike Steen has," the reporter said. "The man's his own boss. He's been handling helicopters for logging companies for years—hauling logs out of the woods, that sort of thing. Then, according to him, one day he decided he didn't like working for someone else. He still hauls logs but only when and where he wants to. In the summer he's kept busy contracting with the forest service and other agencies fighting fires."

What the reporter was describing was a loner, a man with little need for financial security, with confidence in himself, someone who flirted with financial and physical danger. Mike Steen was a man she understood. At least she thought she did.

"I hate to think where we would have been if it hadn't been for him." Lory nodded at the reporter's notebook. "I hope you'll put that in your article."

"You can count on that. But I want this to be more than a story about a helicopter pilot. Mike Steen is here because he's making a lot of money fighting this fire. What about you?"

"Why am I here?" Lory ventured. She'd been asked the question so many times. Surely she should have come up with a credible answer by now. There was one, in her heart, but it just didn't equate well with words.

The reporter smiled and leaned slightly closer. He was tapping her knee with the pencil again, his fingers coming closer than they needed to. His eyes said more than the irritating touch. "That's something I don't understand, Lory. Everyone I talk to says they get a charge out of it, that fire fighting puts excitement into their lives and gives them a challenge."

"It is a challenge." For a moment Lory let silence take over. For the first time in ten hours she was no longer listening to the crackle of flames. The silence was glorious. The last thing she wanted was to have to play man/woman games with this reporter.

"I'm sure it is. But why do *you* do it?"

The man didn't understand. Not at all. "You just listed the reasons."

His smile was meant to be intimate, but it was lost on Lory. "What I listed was why those men over there fight fires. I'd like to know why you're here."

Mike Steen had returned. Lory sensed his presence without having to look for him. She also sensed that he, too, was waiting for her answer. "Because I can't type. Because I hate putting on nylons. Because I'm no different from those men." She stopped for a minute, certain that she wasn't getting her point across, then decided to continue anyway. "I want to do something with my life that matters, that has a purpose, that gives me a charge."

"But—"

"I think she's given you all the answer you need," Mike said as he handed Lory a thermos lid full of ice water. "If I understand what she's saying, men aren't the only ones who need to prove themselves."

"Maybe. But, Lory, we're talking about something that's damn dangerous. Aren't you afraid you might get hurt someday?"

"I could get hurt driving to the grocery store." Lory's stock reply to a stock question usually satisfied everyone but the woman saying the words. She was putting her life on the line every time she went into the woods. Why she continued to do that after Jeff's death was something she wasn't going to ask herself.

She drank deeply and then relinquished the cup so that Mike could refill it. He was standing over her, his legs inches from her limp arms. Saying what she had to say might be easier if she could reach out and touch him.

"I don't have any answer for you." Lory sighed. "At least not one you can put in your article. Because I know you're going to ask it, I'll tell you. Yes, there are times when I'm afraid. There are also times when I'm so hot and tired and thirsty that I swear I'm never going to do it again." This time when Mike handed her the cup their little fingers touched. The contact rejuvenated her. "But then I get some sleep and the next time a call comes in my blood starts pumping again. It doesn't matter whether the fire's man-made or caused by lightning, although a man-made one presents a different kind of confrontation. I can't explain it," she finished up. "I just know I need to do this with my life. I want to do something that has purpose."

Silently Mike joined the two on the grass. Lory. He whispered her name in his mind, trying to get a handle on it. He liked the innate femininity of the word, the gentle way the letters came together. She was a woman who did what was right for her without trying to analyze the reasons, a woman who needed her own kind of goal. He wondered if the reporter could understand that. "I'd suggest we let Ms. Foster go eat," he pointed out firmly. "Do you have any more questions for her?"

Frowning, the reporter relented. "I guess not. Maybe one. Would you recommend that other women get into fire fighting?"

"Only if they aren't afraid of who they are." Lory shifted position, but her thigh muscles lacked the strength to bring her to her feet. It didn't matter. She would curl up on the grass and fall asleep with an earthen mound for a pillow.

But suddenly strong, gentle fingers were on her elbows pulling her to her feet, making her focus on what still needed to be done. For a moment who and what she and Mike Steen were or weren't to each other didn't matter. He was the pillar she needed to lean against. He had the strength she lacked, and he was willing to share that strength.

"Lory," the reporter called out as Mike steered her in the direction of the cafeteria, "one more question. You aren't married, are you?"

Lory was too tired to care why the question was being asked. "No," she said from the shelter of the arm that kept her from collapsing.

"What if you were? Do you think your husband would want you to quit your job?"

"I wouldn't marry him if he didn't understand me any better than that." Lory could have added that the question had never come up between a man and herself, but that wasn't any of the reporter's business.

"But—what if he was afraid for your safety? Haven't you known people who were hurt—"

"I thought you had one more question," Mike interrupted. "That makes two. I haven't eaten since about six this morning and I don't imagine Ms. Foster has, either. I'd say that remedying that is a hell of a lot more important than questions about her marital status."

"Thanks," Lory whispered once they were out of earshot of the reporter. "The questions reporters ask! I wanted to let him know how I felt about the two fools who walked off without making sure their campfire was out. That story might have made an impact. But this—" She shook her head in frustration.

"He didn't respect your privacy. You were a hell of a lot more polite than I would have been."

Lory chuckled low in her throat. "What would you have done? Decked him?"

"Don't tempt me." What was he doing with his arm around Lory Foster? He hadn't known the woman long enough to call her by her first name and yet her hip was bumping against his, her slender shoulders sheltered under his arm. Despite the distraction of the faint scent of talcum, Mike was aware of the look the reporter was sending him. So the man wanted to be where Mike was, doing what Mike was.

Tough. For as long as it took to walk to the cafeteria, he was the one with his arm around Lory Foster. He could no longer remember why he'd been hesitant to leave the familiar isolation of his helicopter.

"I don't know what we should call it," Mike said, suspiciously sniffing the concoction that passed as the main course in the makeshift cafeteria. But filling up the hollows in his stomach was much more important than knowing what was going to accomplish that. "It's a good thing we didn't let that reporter hold you up any longer than he did. The cook's scraping the bottom of the barrel as it is."

Lory followed Mike Steen's lead but went one better. She snagged something that looked like a piece of burger between thumb and forefinger and popped it into her mouth. "It doesn't taste like much of anything," she said after swallowing. She took some of the wilted salad but passed on buttered French bread that looked as if it had been left out since early morning. Eating after being out on the line all day had always been an automatic action, but tonight she was even less aware than usual of what she was putting in her mouth. Still, she remembered to smile at the school cooks who had been called into service to feed the firefighting crews. By the time she was ready to leave the counter, Mike Steen had found an empty cafeteria table at the back of the room.

He'd put his arm around her, deftly pulling her away from intimate questions from the reporter. She should thank him for that. But if she did she would be calling attention to the physical closeness that had taken place. Maybe it had meant no more to him than giving her ice water had.

"What are you doing here?" she asked. In the bright cafeteria lighting she took note of the flecks of brown blending with his predominantly hazel eyes. Nice eyes. Eyes that made contact without probing too deeply. "I didn't hear anything about you coming in to help. Talk about being at the right place at the right time."

Between bites Mike explained that he'd spent the first half of the week fighting a northeastern Washington wildfire and had stopped off at Klamath Falls to look up a former employer. He'd been fueling at the airport when the pilots of the aerial tankers had informed him that the Prospect fire had gotten out of hand. "I called the forest service and was on my way in a half hour."

"Does that happen a lot? I mean, do you just go from one fire to another?"

"Pretty much. I'm centered in Boise, so the Interagency Fire Center keeps me informed on what fires are causing problems. I was getting ready to go home when this thing came up."

"So, are you going to Boise now?" Lory could only hope that her question wouldn't be misinterpreted. She was curious, not, of course, hoping that he'd stay a little longer. Three years of fighting fires had taught her one inescapable fact. Except for those on her own crew, there was no percentage in trying to establish relationships. They wouldn't, couldn't, last.

"That depends," Mike was saying. "I'll call the center in the morning. Who knows where I'll wind up? This is the time of the year I make the most money. I try to make the time count."

Lory nodded in understanding of a man who carried a flight bag filled with the bare essentials because it might be weeks before he was home again. As a combination hot-shot and smoke jumper, Lory was used to being sent almost anywhere in the western United States at a moment's notice. Home base was a house not far from her parents' place along the Snake River in Idaho. During the winter she could indulge in the luxury of sleeping in her own bed, but during a hot, dry summer she was lucky if she was given a cot to sleep on. Still, there were differences. Lory was a forest service employee with job security and supervisors to decide when she would be sent somewhere and what she would do once she was there.

Mike Steen made his own decisions and took his own risks. "The reporter said you also do work for some logging companies," she said. "Do you work year-round?"

"I work when and where I want to." Mike sighed and shook his head. "That sounds good, but it isn't exactly true. Like today. I probably could have taken off this morning and no one would have been the wiser, but I've got this damn sense of responsibility. I don't want to see a forest burn. If there's something I can do, I'll do it."

Lory took another drink of the water she couldn't get enough of but forgot to put down her glass. That was what the reporter hadn't understood. A forest in flames had to be stopped. She and Mike Steen had decided to be part of that effort.

Mike reached over and took the glass out of her hand. "You aren't going to fall asleep, are you?"

"No." Doing things for her came so easy for him. Was it only because she looked so bedraggled? "What you just said," she mused, "that's what I should have told the reporter. I fight fires because someone has to do it and it's something I can do."

"I wouldn't tell that joker anything."

Startled by the sharp edge to Mike's voice, Lory pulled her eyes off the big hand that had almost touched her lips. "Didn't you like him?"

"He was trying to hit on you."

"I know." Despite her effort to dismiss what Mike had said, Lory wound up laughing. "I think the poor man has a knee fetish. If Keith ever does that to me again—"

"Keith?"

"The crew foreman. He told me this reporter was going to want to talk to me. I told him I wasn't interested but—"

"Why not, Lory? Why didn't you want to talk to him?"

Her name spoken by Mike Steen sounded different from the way it had when the reporter had stopped calling her Ms.

Foster. "I don't like talking about myself. Having it pointed out that I'm a woman in a man's job, well, that old line has gotten pretty threadbare."

"And you don't like being hit on."

"No, I don't. It's a cheap game."

"A lot of people think it's a necessary game." Mike pushed aside his plate before leaning his elbows on the table. He was close enough that Lory could make out the faint haze of stubble. Would it feel rough if she touched his cheek?

"There are other ways for people to get to know each other," Lory pointed out.

"Such as?"

"Such as talking the way we are." Too late Lory realized how her words might be interpreted. Would Mike think that sharing dinner and conversation with him was her way of hitting on a man? He wouldn't if he was perceptive, but Lory didn't know him well enough to answer that. "I enjoy conversation," she hurried on. "There's a lot of time for that while we're flying to a fire or waiting to be called. We don't do much talking on the line. Just about showers and ice cream."

Mike refilled Lory's glass from the icy pitcher on the table and pushed her plate aside before speaking. "What do you talk about?"

Lory laughed. "Everything. Nothing. We make outrageous bets on baseball games. We argue makes of cars and complain about paying taxes. And we talk about the fires. We—" Her smile was open. "We dream up punishments for those who set fires. The Indians had a pretty good idea with their anthills."

At the front of the room the cooks started clearing away the meal. The sound of clattering pots and pans tore through the quiet conversation taking place at the rear of the cafeteria. Although it was the last thing he wanted to do, Mike pushed himself to his feet and walked around to Lory's end of the table. This time she was on her feet before he could reach for her. He let her lead the way out of the building without touching her.

The night air smelled faintly of smoke, but the sounds they heard were of men laughing, not yelling. The fire was coming to an end. Mike would spend the night in the gymnasium turned dormitory, get up in the morning, then take off. There was nothing to keep him here. Nothing except a weary young woman who maybe didn't care whether he left or not.

"What happens to you now?" Mike asked, bending toward her. "Where do you go tomorrow?"

"I don't know. Wherever they send us."

She was looking up at him, but there was no invitation, nothing to encourage him to cover her soft lips with his own. Or maybe there was and he simply didn't know how to read the message. "You don't mind living like a gypsy?"

Lory shook her head. The now-dry mass moved with life and electricity, stopping Mike's thoughts. "It's what I do, Mike."

Mike. His name would never sound the same again.

Chapter Two

For someone accustomed to sleeping anywhere at anytime,
Lory found sleep an elusive mist that slipped through her
fingers every time she thought she'd captured it. She and
Ann Larsen were sharing one of the school's rubber exer-
cise mats, which was softer than some of the places she'd
been in her years of fire fighting. Because of the number of
bodies in the poorly ventilated building, even a single blan-
ket was too warm. Still, Lory couldn't blame the heat, having to sleep in her clothes for the sake of modesty or even the
noise practically in her ear. Ann had given her a blow-by-
blow account of the telephone conversation she'd had with
her husband, but was now snoring in short bursts. When
Ann had first joined the crew, her snoring had been the
source of more than one joke, but Lory should have been
tired enough to sleep in the middle of a rock band.

But that was impossible. Somewhere in the darkened
room a tall, solid helicopter pilot with oversize hands and a
face fashioned from a slice of granite was sleeping. Mike
Steen wasn't handsome. His bone structure was excellent,
strong and solid, but the flesh over it was too much like
leather to conform to modern advertising standards. Jeans,
boots, shirts grabbed off the nearest rack during the few
occasions when he entered a clothing store, all of these obviously suited him. Whatever went on in his head had very

little to do with the physical package, though. What stayed with Lory was the understanding that Mike consisted of many layers, none of them easily revealed.

That and not sore muscles and Ann's snoring was the problem. Lory couldn't sleep because she couldn't get Mike Steen out of her mind. What did she know about the man? That he was self-employed and lived in Boise and knew how to fly a helicopter big enough to lift entire trees out of the wilderness. That a shave didn't get him through the day and he didn't think much of men who hit on women they didn't know.

It wasn't enough.

He hadn't said whether he was married, although Lory didn't think he was, since home base meant so little. Still, there might be a woman somewhere. Parents. Sisters and brothers. Friends. Where had he grown up, how much schooling had he had and how had he learned to fly helicopters?

What did she care? She wasn't going to see him after tomorrow anyway. This was hardly the first time someone had slipped in and out of her life.

When the dimly lit clock over a basketball hoop at the far end of the gym said 3:16 a.m., Lory stopped lying to herself. She did care. For only the second time in her life she wanted to know what ticked inside a man. She didn't want him to fly out of her life in the morning. Not until she knew more. But she had no idea how to tell him that.

"YOU OWN THAT OUTRIGHT. No bank loan hanging over your head?" Mike Steen and Boyd Doughtery were standing next to the Sikorsky while the rising sun turned the tinted bubble glass from dusky rose to bright orange. Lory's fellow smoke jumper had followed Mike outside while the pilot had radioed the interagency center. Now Boyd was trying to turn the massive blades manually while Mike watched. "Someday I'd like to be my own boss."

"Get yourself an accountant. The paperwork will drive you crazy." As he spoke, Mike assimilated what he'd heard from Boise. There had been a series of lightning strikes in Montana overnight, but nothing that personnel already there couldn't handle. If he wanted the job, the Bureau of Land Management could use him in eastern Oregon to control some grass fires fanned by high winds. He'd probably take it. His job here was finished, and after a decent night's sleep Mike was once more restless. If he didn't have something to do, he'd just as soon be on his way.

He'd long been drawn to the desolation of high desert country with more deer and antelope than people, and people who knew more about hay and cattle than where the President was spending the weekend. Maybe, if there was time, he'd take some aerial photography of the antelope herds.

Boyd gave up on the blades and shrugged. "Who am I kidding? My wife would have a fit if I tied all our money up in a chopper. Besides, this is my last year fighting fires. In the fall I'm turning into a desk jockey and hanging up my shovel."

"Doesn't your wife like you fighting fires?" Mike asked. Mike wasn't sure how he felt about having company this early, but Boyd had followed him out of the gym and obviously felt he had a right to tinker with the Sikorsky. Telling Boyd to keep his hands off would be rude.

"It isn't that." Boyd rubbed an imaginary smear off the Plexiglas door with his elbow. "She's a game control officer, so she knows about risk taking, but we've got a baby on the way. That's going to mean a lot of changes. Someone depending on us. We agreed that it isn't fair to a baby to be living out of a suitcase. We're both going to be pushing pencils from now on."

Mike tried to see himself sitting behind a desk. Because he'd never done it, he had nothing for comparison, but maybe if he had children he would be reevaluating how he lived his life. Children? That was also something he'd never given a lot of thought. Mike liked children as much as the next man. He just didn't know what it would feel like to have his life revolve around a child, to have someone dependent on him.

He asked Boyd how he and his wife had met. Then the two men started back toward the cafeteria where they'd been promised fresh cups of coffee. As they passed the gym, Mike's eyes strayed to where Lory might still be sleeping.

"She's up."

Mike turned. He hadn't known Lory was on his mind until Boyd had brought her up. "You think so? It's pretty early."

"Hartigan came looking for her. I guess there's a problem just north of here. An arson fire it looks like. If you want to see her, you'd better grab her soon. She's not going to be here much longer."

"Where's she going?" Mike asked, nerves unaccountably alert. Arson, even for a man involved only with the mop-up of forest fires, wasn't something he liked to hear. "If there's another fire, aren't all of you going?"

"Not this time," Boyd explained as the men entered the cafeteria. "It wasn't much of a fire, I guess. But Lory's an arson specialist. She gets called into one of these things several times a year."

Over steaming coffee and French toast, Mike mulled over what Boyd had said. He'd been impressed by the female fire fighter's competence yesterday, and now a new dimension had been added. It was a good thing the reporter hadn't known about Lory's specialty. Otherwise the man might still be asking questions. "What does an arson expert do?" he asked after a lengthy silence. "I don't see what good it does to know if a fire's deliberately set if you can't catch the bastard who did it."

Boyd chuckled. "Ask Lory. Get her going on that and you'll never get her to shut up. You like the lady?"

What was with Boyd Doughtery? Mike wondered. Didn't the man have enough to do running his own life without poking his nose into other people's business? But because Boyd had shown him a picture of his wife and told him the prospective names of his unborn child, Mike was unable to think of an effective way to squelch the man's curiosity. "It depends on what you mean by like. I just met her."

"Yeah, but she sticks with you. Look—" Boyd leaned forward, his voice low "—you aren't the only one who feels like that about Lory Foster. Not only is she one good-looking woman, but, well, if you knew certain things, you couldn't help but care and want things to come out right for her."

"What certain things?"

"Ask her. Get her to talk about it if you can." Boyd laughed at himself. "I don't mean to make a mystery out of this, but I'm talking about something that's a lot more Lory's business than mine. She's the one who went through it. When and if Lory feels like talking about it, I don't want you second-guessing her emotions."

"How can I second-guess her?" Mike pointed out. "She's got to go look at this arson thing and I'm going to be leaving within the hour."

"So come back. Or find out where she's sent next and join her."

Run after Lory? Boyd might think he was being helpful, but Mike was a long way from wanting anyone to play matchmaker for him. When, and if, he hooked up with a woman it would be because he wanted to. So far the desire to be part of one person's life had never surfaced. He side-stepped the issue by asking Boyd to send him a copy of the newspaper article if the hotshot team was still in the area when it came out.

He was debating having another cup of coffee before leaving when Lory and a man in slacks and golf shirt entered the cafeteria. The two were engaged in a sober conversation, their shoulders brushing as they reached for coffee cups. Lory's stance said it all. She was an equal partner in the conversation. A few minutes later, after they'd selected their breakfasts, they looked for a place to sit. When Boyd waved his hand, the two made their way to the table.

The jeans Lory was wearing were probably the same ones she'd had on last night, but the shirt had been exchanged for a soft cotton blouse open at the throat as a defense against the heat that had already reached the small town. She looked rested this morning. Younger. More animated. And utterly, undeniably, feminine. When Lory smiled at him, Mike forgot everything except how much warmth had been in her slender shoulders when he'd touched her the previous night.

Boyd stood to shake hands with the newcomer and then introduced him to Mike. Sheppard Banks was employed by the local power company. It was he who had gone to the county sheriff with his concerns that a small fire he'd spotted around dawn had been arson. Although the sheriff had already put in a call to Lory, Sheppard had come in person to explain the situation.

"I'm still kicking myself for not taking down that license number," he told the others. "But I don't suppose that's necessary. I know the kids who were driving that red VW. I've been driving that county road for five years, and that's the first time I've seen those kids out at that time of the morning."

"Is the fire out?" Mike asked. He didn't have to leave right now. He could learn a little something about arson and what Lory Foster was being asked to do before he took off. He could see if she still smelled like talcum.

Sheppard nodded. "I was almost to the Prospect city limits. I used the CB on my brother's truck to call their volunteer fire department. Now, as I understand it, it's up to Lory to determine if it was arson. Bill, that's the sheriff, said he'd take over, but this is the most excitement I've had so far this year. I'm eager to see how an arson investigator works."

"I hope you aren't expecting too much," Lory warned Sheppard. "If you're looking for a Hollywood-type investigation, you're going to be disappointed. I'm not promising anything at this point."

Mike's voice was soft, but not so soft that it didn't register in a way the others' hadn't. "What's with it with people?" he asked. "There's been a whole forest in danger of going up in smoke this week. You'd think that would satisfy the crazies."

"It doesn't," she answered him. "And don't ask me to explain the reasons, because that's something I'll never understand." Lory concentrated on her coffee, even though she couldn't taste or feel it. Her first thought when Keith had come looking for her was whether Mike Steen had left yet. She hadn't thought so because she hadn't heard the chopper take off, but since she'd finally managed to doze off just before dawn she hadn't been certain.

It shouldn't matter that he was still here, but it did. There was a fresh grease stain on his jeans high up on one thigh. He'd probably been checking out his chopper and would be leaving as soon as breakfast was over. So what? Having people come and go was a way of life for her. She'd had conversations with men before. The one she and Mike had shared last night wasn't any different.

In response to something Boyd was saying about an arson fire in the same general area last year, Lory shook off the cobwebs. Mike hadn't come looking for her this morning. That should tell her all she needed to know about how he viewed last night. "That wasn't really arson," she said. Boyd was the one she should be talking to. Why then was she looking at Mike? And why was he looking at her? "If I remember correctly, it was a couple of little kids with matches. I met the sheriff while I was investigating that one. He's an interesting man. I don't know how he finds the time to do all the fishing he does."

"They were teenagers, not little kids." Boyd brought the conversation back on line. "A thirteen-year-old knows what a match can do."

"What happened to them?" Mike asked. "You caught them, didn't you?"

Lory smiled. "Not me. I can't take the credit for that. It isn't part of my job. I just did the legwork. In cases like that the court usually assesses the parents for the damage. My guess is those kids are still grounded."

"Maybe they learned something. When do you have to leave?"

Lory glanced at the power-company employee for confirmation. "Not long. Sheppard's going to take me back to where he saw the Volkswagen and then I'm going to take a look at the burn area. What about you?" Lory forced out the question that she hadn't wanted to ask. "Are you leaving soon?"

"I should. The BLM wants me."

The conversation was everyday. Why didn't she feel everyday? "Sounds interesting."

"Not as interesting as what you're doing today. How did you get into this arson investigation business?"

Because Lory had been asked the question before, the answer came without her having to think about it. She'd attended a couple of training sessions that had focused on arson investigation, and then when she'd heard that an interagency statewide workshop was being planned, she signed up for that. The workshop had lasted the better part of a week, and Lory had come away with a wealth of knowledge she was now eager to share, especially in sparsely populated areas where the law-enforcement agency didn't have an arson specialist on staff. "It's a lot like crime investigation," she wound up. "We dig and dig and hopefully the pieces fit together. Not too exciting, I'm afraid."

"But you like it, don't you?"

"Yes, I enjoy it. I like being presented with a challenge."

As Mike nodded his agreement, Lory's eyes fixed on his shoulders. She spent her life surrounded by physically able men. One set of broad, competent shoulders shouldn't mean more than the others. He was saying something about the rugged life-style of those who lived in eastern Oregon where he would be heading in a few minutes, but Lory was unable to give his words the attention she should have. They'd shared words last night. This morning she wanted more. Something to keep.

Lory knew as well as anyone else here that friendships among fire fighters were both intense and transient. When they were together on the fire line, it was second nature to look out for each other's safety. A lot came out during the flights to major fire areas when whole crews of fire fighters wrestled with the reality that this time they might not come back. Last week Lory had told a total stranger about trying to survive despite four older brothers who refused to accept her lesser physical strength. Now she couldn't remember what that man looked like.

Lory was tired of living like that. She wanted to make another friendship that lasted longer than the time it took to put out a fire. She wanted to know she could call someone up in the middle of winter and pick up where they'd left off. She wanted—another Jeff.

No, she didn't. Lory didn't ever want to hurt like that again.

Swallowing a sigh that came too close to being a sob, Lory rose to her feet and jammed her hands into her back pockets. She was unaware of the way the gesture thrust her hips forward. The only thing she knew was that she had to get away from her thoughts. "We'd better get going, Sheppard." Unbidden, her eyes found Mike Steen. She'd said goodbye a thousand times. It shouldn't be that hard, but this time it was. Maybe Mike would show her how to accomplish what was fast becoming impossible. "I . . . hope you're around the next time a fire gets out of control," she said lamely.

Mike was on his feet, too. He didn't speak as he came around the table and placed his arm over Lory's shoulder. "Glad to be of service, ma'am. Just be happy you're not the one getting my bill." Using his body as a buffer, he separated Lory from the other two men and steered her toward the front door. Lory kept her hands jammed in her pockets as insurance against the urge to loop her fingers through the waistband riding low on his hips.

"I enjoyed last night," Mike whispered. He'd turned toward her just enough so that she was able to feel his breath against the top of her head. "What you said about wanting a challenge—I think it made an impression on the reporter. He wasn't expecting that from a woman."

"I enjoyed last night, too." Was there anything else she should say? Any way of stretching out the moment?

They were outside now, standing off to one side of the large door. Men were still coming into the cafeteria. Lory nodded at a couple of them but made no attempt to separate herself from Mike's arm. She wondered if her shoulder would carry his imprint for the rest of the day. "This fire you're going to today," she asked, "is it a big one?"

Mike explained that wind conditions and not the size of the fire were what had the BLM concerned. He had no explanation for why he'd risked refusal by seeking these last minutes alone with her, only that he wouldn't be able to get into the Sikorsky without having tried.

The silent battle taking place within him threw Mike for a loop. In the past month he'd been to every western state except Nevada and said hello and goodbye to dozens of people. He'd shared a beer and a joke with some of them, dated two female forest service employees and taken a group of retarded children for a ride in his chopper. He'd enjoyed those contacts, but when the time to leave came his mind was already on what was ahead.

This time he was thinking about what he would be leaving behind.

"We live in the same state," he was saying. "You'd think our paths would have crossed by now."

"Maybe they have. To you all of us on the ground must look like ants."

Mike didn't remember her voice being that weak. Was she, too, dreading the moment when they'd have to shake hands, or was she merely anxious to be out on the county road? He said something about getting within a hundred feet of the ground during a lot of his drops and being able to see a lot more than antlike creatures, but he didn't care what he was saying or what she might say in turn.

God, she was soft. Soft and strong. He remembered how vulnerable she had looked last night with exhaustion etched on her face and then thought about the kind of competence it took to be considered an arson expert. She was, he decided, more strength than vulnerability. "Where do you go after this?" he asked.

"I'm not sure," Lory answered him. This was insane. She'd been the one to tell Sheppard they should be getting on the road and now she was content to lean against a cafeteria wall with a man's hand draped over her shoulder. "I'm slated to go home later today, but that's subject to change. It's so dry in Washington. I wouldn't be surprised if we're sent there. I'd make a good travel agent. Name anywhere in the western states and I've been there."

"How does your family feel about that? Does it bother them the way you earn your living?"

That was one question Lory could answer easily. Usually she didn't bother with an explanation of the forces that had shaped her, but she'd like Mike Steen to know—if only there was time. "They're all for it. They've always said they raised hyperactive kids. Dad says it was either this or having a daughter who rides the rails."

"My mom says I take after my father. He was a restless man."

Lory forgot to breathe. She didn't know how she knew it, but she was certain Mike was telling her something not many people knew. "You said was. Is your father dead?"

"He might be."

You don't want to talk about this, do you? Lory asked silently. If she knew Mike better, if they had more time, she might be able to break through this barrier. But they were brand-new to each other, and new was all they were ever going to be. "What about your mother?" She deliberately steered the conversation onto what she thought was a safe path. "Does what you do bother her?"

"It bothers both of us. Not—" Mike turned toward Lory. He bent his head slightly so that they were looking into each other's eyes. Someone entering the cafeteria called out Lory's name. She didn't acknowledge him. "Not the danger aspect, because Mom doesn't see what I do as dangerous, but the being apart," Mike was saying. "She says I have to do what I have to do, but it was just Mom and me when I was growing up. I worry about her."

"You could get another job. Be around more."

"No, I couldn't, Lory. I tried that once. I worked for a logging company that was in turn owned by some conglomerate. I just went crazy trying to keep up with all the regulations.''

"Then you're a gypsy, too." *Oh, Mike, we could have something. It's there, just beyond our reach.*

"Mom says I'm a drifter. No." He increased the pressure on her shoulder just enough for it to register as a gentle squeeze. "I don't think it's that. I like having a home base. I just don't need to be there very often." His voice, already soft, dropped to a whisper. "My mother is the only real tie I have, but she's independent, too. You'd like her house. She bought this dump and fixed it up by herself. She's a teacher. A damn good one. She says they're going to have to shoot her to get her to retire."

Lory chuckled because she needed to feel something other than the seriousness Mike was handing her. The thought she'd had a moment ago frightened her because it exposed holes she didn't want to know she had. They were getting so close so fast. If it couldn't last any longer than this morning, she didn't want it. "My mom taught for a few years, but she got tired of the bureaucratic red tape and parents wanting her to do their job for them. Now she and dad own a snowmobile business and goof off all summer. Actually they charter rafting trips on the Snake, but I refuse to believe that's work."

"They sound like my kind of people," Mike said. His lips were inches from hers. If she made the move, would he respond?

Before the question could be answered, the cafeteria door opened and Sheppard and Boyd came out. "That has to be the worst coffee I've had in a month," Boyd said while Sheppard made a move toward his car. Lory felt Mike's hand slip off her shoulder. Shaken by what she'd been so close to doing, Lory started after Sheppard.

Think of something. You at least have to say goodbye. Make him understand that you've left someone before and will do it again. Slowly Lory turned back around to find Mike still leaning against the cafeteria wall. He was looking at her. "If you see Greg Harper, say hello to him for me," she told him. "He's some kind of biologist with the BLM in Deschutes County. Tell him I said he's the worst poker player in three states."

Mike nodded gravely, as if delivering Lory's message was the most important thing he had to do that day. With a grunt, he pushed himself away from the wall. "Wait a minute. I'll walk you to the car. How do you know about this Greg Harper's poker-playing ability?"

"It's legendary. We killed a couple of days playing poker while waiting for lightning strikes that never materialized. I hate cards and I'm ten times better than he'll ever be." The trek to Sheppard's vehicle didn't take nearly long enough. Lory didn't know how she felt about having the other two men with them, but she wasn't sure she wanted to be alone with Mike, either.

Finally there was nothing to do but get into the car, wind down the window and look up at Mike. Her mind had been racing with a thousand possibilities for getting the necessary words out of the way, but now that the time had arrived she didn't want to say anything. If he couldn't read her thoughts, then no amount of words on her part would make any difference. She sighed faintly, eyes squinting against the morning sun. He seemed more shadow and blur than flesh and blood. Forgetting him should be easier this way.

"What you're going to do today," he asked, "is it ever dangerous?"

Lory had been asked that question before, but this was the first time she wanted to give more than the standard reply. She had to choose her words carefully. There was a small measure of danger in dealing with those who would deliberately set a fire, but most arsonists acted impulsively. Seldom did they think ahead to the consequences should they be caught. There was only one brand of arsonist capable of making the hairs on the back of Lory's head stand on end.

"It can be," she said as honestly as possible. "Criminals sometimes use the national forests. If they set a fire to hide evidence of what they're doing, or to try to burn out the competition... So far I haven't had to deal with any of them, but they're getting bold. And a little desperate because of the crackdown on drugs."

Mike's eyes darkened. Don't take chances, he wanted to tell her. Let someone else take the risks. But in the few hours he'd known Lory, he'd learned something. She made any and all decisions about her life. There was only one thing left to say. "Take care of yourself, Lory."

"I will. Take care of yourself, Mike."

The car engine started. Feeling hollowed out, Lory turned away, deliberately concentrating on the way out. She didn't know when Mike stepped back or whether he stayed to watch her departure. Sheppard was saying something about the quick work the volunteer fire department had done putting out the blaze, but talking to the man next to her was beyond Lory.

She couldn't chalk her reaction up to last night's exhaustion. On the surface, Mike Steen wasn't that different from the other men she came across in her job. True, there was a certain fascination about the way he earned his living, and he was the epitome of ruggedness, but that was the outer shell. She didn't know him well enough to have any idea what went on inside him. How was it possible to be mesmerized by a man she'd known for less than a day?

It wasn't.

By the time they reached the site of the burn, Lory had been able to shake most of herself free from the fog she was in, but she continued to function in a robotlike way. Sheppard was still excited by the way his day had begun, and he filled up whatever gaps might have occurred in the conversation.

He explained that his car had had a dead battery that morning and he'd had to borrow his visiting brother's truck to get to work. It was just getting light when he passed the VW with its three teenage passengers. He was surprised when they didn't wave at him until he realized that his brother's truck wasn't one they'd recognize. Just as he was shaking his head over the speed the boys were traveling, he came across the small fire burning some twenty feet back from the quiet county road. He had grown up in the woods; he knew that moments counted when it came to extinguishing fires during a dry summer. Before the flames had time to reach the trees, the volunteer fire department was on the job.

"I don't have anything concrete to go on," the sheriff told Lory when she and Sheppard joined him near the charred grass. "We have a suspicious fire and a car speeding out of the area, but maybe it was caused by a cigarette. For that, the kids, if it's them, get a slap on the wrist. But if they did this deliberately, I want it stopped. I want the word to get around that starting fires is no damn joke."

Lory agreed. After being assured that the local fire department had left the area untouched after putting the fire out, she began walking slowly over the site, eyes alert for signs the untrained wouldn't notice. A few minutes later she grunted and dropped to her knees. She pulled a pocketknife from her back pocket and dug into the earth. She repeated the same process in two other places and turned the small dirty ends of three candles over to the sheriff. "It was deliberate all right," she said tersely. "Someone stuck the candles into the ground, lit them and waited for the candles to burn down. My guess is they had matches ringing the candles. Once those went off, the dry conditions took care of the rest."

Sheppard whistled. "How did you know where to dig?"

"I didn't at first," Lory explained. "But if you'll look closely, you'll see that there are three origins for the fire. Three separate fires with three different cores. That's no accident."

The sheriff was holding the candle ends in his palm. "That was fast work."

"Those kids were careless. They probably sat here watching the candles burn and then took off when the matches went off. I'd like to think they knew they'd made a mistake, that the fires weren't going to go out of their own accord. Of course having Sheppard showing up so soon made my work a lot easier. Now comes the hard part," she reminded the sheriff. "Getting those kids to own up to what they did."

"Who knows?" the sheriff said as they headed back toward the vehicles. "Maybe there'll be other candles in the VW. It's amazing what comes out if the kids are questioned separately, especially if they believe there's been a witness." He patted Sheppard on the shoulder. "I owe you one."

"Get him to take you to one of his fishing spots," Lory suggested to Sheppard. "I'd like to know if there's anything to all this boasting I've heard." She sighed. "It's been so long since I've gone fishing. That's a terrible thing for someone who lives near a river to have to admit."

The sheriff, who recognized Lory from the last time they'd worked together, offered to include her in the fishing trip, but Lory had to turn him down. Besides, with parents who made their living off the river, fishing was something she could do every time she went home. Fishing. Rafting. It wasn't a bad idea. "If someone will take me back to the school, I might be able to leave with my crew. I don't think you're going to need me any more, do you?"

"Probably not. I don't think these kids are going to lie very long. I know them. They're not bad. Just bored. And stupid. You're sure you won't be able to join us?"

"Don't tempt me. Sorry. You know this is the busy time of the year for us. I have to plan my time off carefully. My parents are hoping to get us all together for a river trip soon. They'll really be hurt if I don't make that."

"That's right," the sheriff teased. "Leave me here with all the work while you go flying all over the country. You probably make more with overtime and hazard pay in a summer than I do all year."

Lory shook her head. "I doubt that. At least you get to stay in one place." Silently she slipped into the passenger's side of the sheriff's car. She loved her job, but there were drawbacks. One drawback, she amended. Being called on to be anywhere within the western states left no time for developing relationships, for learning what lay below the surface in a pair of piercing hazel eyes.

Chapter Three

On the fifth day fire crews from the Bureau of Indian Affairs were sent in to assist those already fighting the Saddle Mountain fire. Those who had been on the fire line for the better part of a week were aware that planes had landed reinforcements who would be climbing the ridge to where they were trying to cut off the fire's advance, but the news gave little comfort. In this, the most persistent fire of the still-young season, there was no guarantee that more manpower would bring the blaze under control.

Lory was one of seventy-five fighting the lightning-caused, creeping behemoth. Assisted by bulldozers and a half-dozen air tankers dropping retardant, a line was being drawn between the fire and the tinder-dry forest in its path. The computer program known as BEHAVE had predicted the speed, path and intensity of the fire. That knowledge plus RAWS, or Remote Automated Weather Stations, added greatly to the command post's knowledge of wind speed and direction, humidity and air temperature.

On the line only one thing mattered. Gaining control before the fire created its own wind current and made the last-ditch technique of lighting backfires a dangerous necessity. Oblivious to the weight of their packs, Lory and her fellow fire fighters were intent on hot-spotting. Brush, trees and dry tinder were being cleared from the path of the fastest burning flame fingers. Once those short sections had been constructed, they were connected to create a frontal barrier. Only then could the fire fighters' attention be turned to the flanks and rear and containment be achieved. If the wind didn't turn on them, that is.

Once again Boyd Doughtery was nearby, but today he was doing little talking. The pressure of roping a giant left little energy for anything except what had to be done. Lory wished she could take time to talk to her friend, say something to ease his concern, but she had to think of conserving her energy first. Boyd had been unable to contact his wife since coming to Saddle Mountain. He was worried that Sal's not knowing where he was would make her anxious.

"She's used to it," Lory gasped as they dropped back for relatively fresher air. "This isn't the first time you've been out of touch."

"I know," Boyd acknowledged. "But I keep thinking about the baby. Will her worrying be bad for it?"

"Sal's a levelheaded woman. She's not sitting around wringing her hands."

"I know," Boyd repeated. "But Lory—" He stopped as an engulfed tree crashed to the earth. "It's different for me now with the baby. Do you ever think about not making it back sometime?"

Lory had been faced with that question once before. Had it slammed into her heart and gut. She'd prayed she'd never have to face that again. "You know I have."

Boyd turned his back on the downed giant and concentrated on what he could do to save those that were left. "I'm sorry. Bad question. But that's what I'm thinking about. I know it probably isn't going to happen, but what if Sal has to raise our child alone? What if I never see my son or daughter? Damn it, Lory! That baby deserves a father."

The need to press forward put an end to the conversation, but Lory was unable to shake Boyd's words. Last year she'd had a friend to tell her feelings to, to talk about maybe not making it out of the forest. Boyd knew that. Her friend was no longer alive, and Lory had learned to keep certain emotions to herself. It wasn't that she wanted to deny Boyd the opportunity to voice his fears—every fire fighter had to deal with that—but Jeff's death had brought her face-to-face with mortality. She was no longer able to expose herself the way Boyd was doing. For her, death was no longer an abstract. Instead, she focused on the boiling smoke around her and thought about how a tree can become a resinous torch.

Enough of that! Lory arched her back against the weight on her shoulders and shut down her mind. In a half hour she'd have a drink from her canteen. In two hours she'd try to remember the jerky she'd shoved in her backpack this morning. Until the crew took time for a break, she would do what she'd been trained to do and nothing else.

She wouldn't think about Jeff.

Three hours later Lory and Boyd were washing jerky down with water when their crew chief brought word that the Sikorsky that had helped out two weeks ago was back again. "I understand Center put out the call for him and a couple other choppers that had just finished with that rangeland fire to the east. RAWS says that weather system they were worried about is definitely kicking up. We've got to get this beast under control before the lightning strikes start. What we don't need is any more wind."

"When's he going to be here?" Lory asked as she resettled her pack and picked up her shovel. "It's getting pretty late in the day." Mike Steen, she added silently. The man with the soft, steady name.

"Pretty damn soon. I guess they've been keeping tabs on this fire thinking they might be needed. If things go the way they figure, they should be dropping retardant in less than an hour. You haven't seen him since we ran into him in Oregon, have you?"

"How could I?" Keith was a good man but inclined to be a little too nosy. "We've been on the move constantly."

"Just asking, Lory. Just asking." Keith patted her shoulder. "Maybe you'll see him tonight."

I'm not counting on it, Lory thought as Keith moved on down the line. Granted, Lory was next to impossible to track down during a heavy fire season, but if Mike Steen wanted to leave a message, he knew how. If he didn't, she would accept his decision, and if he did . . . Lory glanced skyward at least three times before committing her body to the seemingly never-ending task.

MIKE WAS LEANING over his controls trying to see around the billowing smoke. As fires went, this one was fairly sedate. It was massive, with convection columns billowing thousands of feet into the sky, but set so that wind drafts couldn't easily grip the flames. It could kick up its own wind currents, though, if they didn't get a handle on it soon. Then there was the summer lightning storm RAWS was predicting. Put the two together and the slumbering beast could become a raging giant.

That, in part, was why he was here. Mike smelled smoke, saw the flames pushing through lodgepole and fir, heard the explosion of tinder-dry ground fuels and wondered at the self-control it took to keep a fire fighter standing his ground.

Or her ground. Lory Foster was down there somewhere. Without really understanding why, Mike had remembered the name of Lory's crew chief. It hadn't taken long for the dispatcher at the command center to relay the information that Keith Hartigan's crew had been one of the first to reach the fire. That meant Lory had been at Saddle Mountain for at least five days.

Firedance

Mike, too, had been in Idaho most of that time, but the rangeland fire caused by a backfiring tractor had been a pesky one fueled by winds racing across the prairie. They'd done pretty well as long as the water supply in several nearby reservoirs had held out, but once that was gone, Mike and the other pilots had had to travel close to fifty miles for another water supply. He'd been in the air so long that his body felt welded to the seat, but that was nothing compared to the strain the ground crew here must be under.

Nothing compared to what Lory was asking her body to do.

Mike didn't know what to do with his thoughts. It wasn't like him to think about someone once they were no longer together. After flying out of Prospect, he'd toyed with the idea of trying to get in touch with Lory again, but couldn't think of a valid reason for picking up the phone. He'd never called a woman simply to hear her voice.

Today he didn't need a reason. Lory was one of the ants surrounded by fire. He wanted her out of there as soon as possible.

Dipping almost to the treetops, Mike followed the instructions given him by the command center. He was to drop retardant directly in front of the fire's path, but because the fire had just shifted direction, the coordinates he had been given were less than exact. He'd have to go by sight if the hundreds of gallons of retardant swinging under him were to do any good.

Through the smoke he could make out a hot river of flame coasting downhill, and he reached for the lever that would upend the sloshing bag. At the last moment the smoke broke away. He could make out a loose knot of men staring up at him. Saluting smartly, Mike banked upward before attacking the flames from another direction. The last thing the fire fighters needed was bright, sticky retardant dropped on them.

Ten minutes later Mike was back again. The mountain lake he'd just dipped out of was behind the fire but close enough that the fire wouldn't have shifted direction in the time he was gone. This load was released just to the left of the first one. He spotted several fire fighters waving at him but wasn't close enough to identify any of them. Before he could go back for another load, he was instructed to drop on an area a quarter of a mile away.

The rest of the afternoon went that way with Mike and the other choppers being shotgunned around, sometimes criss-crossing one another's path because the fire had more than one point of advance. Although Mike was accustomed to being deployed in this manner, he found it irritating. Over the years he'd formed his own game plan for using his chopper most efficiently. There were reasons why he was self-employed, not the least of which was a basic dislike for taking orders, but with the ominous weather system building to the north and threatening to become reality sometime tomorrow, this wasn't the time to argue. He didn't want Lory down there when and if lightning struck.

"You want to call it a wrap?" one of the other pilots asked over the radio as the sun was setting. "I'm getting low on fuel."

"Me, too," Mike acknowledged. "They're going to feed us, aren't they?"

"They'd better. And there better be more than butter sandwiches. Lord I hate those things."

Mike agreed. Because mayonnaise turned rancid without refrigeration, sandwiches on the fire line were made with butter. Unless there was nothing else available Mike avoided them. As he waited his turn to land on the helipad a tractor had made for the choppers, Mike's mind slid back to the meal he'd shared with Lory Foster. There had been some kind of salad—that much he remembered—but the rest of the food was a blank.

Not so the woman he'd sat across a cafeteria table from.
It had been hard to make out what she looked like when
he'd first seen her sooty face, but when she'd stepped out of
the gym and lifted her wet hair off her shoulders, he'd
understood why she stood out. Not many women built like
that risked their slight bodies on a fire line.

Slight but strong, Mike corrected. And independent. After all, she hadn't tried to contact him. Probably she
wouldn't remember who he was.

There were at least five times the number of personnel at
the Saddle Mountain command center than there had been
at Prospect. After wandering in and out of the knots of
people for fifteen minutes, Mike gave up. He hadn't eaten
since last night; certainly that was more important than
finding one woman. He hooked up with the pilots of the
other two helicopters and eased into the line in front of the
two catering trucks that were dispensing food. The wilderness area, accessible only by a logging road, was a mass of
humanity with an even longer line in front of the watering
truck, which served as the only shower. The two men cur-
rently under the shower had stripped to their shorts and were
enduring catcalls from those waiting their turn. The one
semiflat area served as sleeping quarters. Even in the midst
of evening activity, tired fire fighters were already buried in
their sleeping bags.

Most, however, were forming small groups around their
belongings. The hum of conversation was occasionally
snuffed out as vehicles either left or entered the center.
Those who had already picked up their dinners leaned their
weary backs against their packs as they ate.

It was in one of those groups that Mike found Lory. He'd
picked up a plate filled with something that passed for spa-
ghetti and was following the other pilots through the maze
when something without form or substance reached out and
stopped him.

Mike turned and looked down. Lory was staring back up at him, part of a hard roll caught between her teeth. Wet, clean hair hugged the sides of her face. The eyes that had been deep caves the first time he'd seen her had turned into bottomless caverns etched with exhaustion. She had probably showered with her sleeveless T-shirt on; the still-damp fabric clung to her slender shoulders and gave away the secrets of her full, unrestrained breasts. She was barefoot. So, he thought, she was out of the forest for tonight at least. He wanted to think he had had something to do with that.

It was him. Lory had seen the chopper land, but conversation and the promise of cool water cascading over her had diverted her. By the time she'd emerged from behind the hand-held blankets that offered a measure of privacy, she'd lost sight of the pilots. And there had been dozens of acquaintances to speak to while she had located the rest of her belongings and waited her turn for something to eat.

She'd wanted to go looking for Mike, but a shyness Lory couldn't explain had taken hold of her. She'd been able to say words of greeting to at least twenty men since coming into camp, but what she'd said to them hadn't taken any thought. They were men she could share a few minutes of conversation with without feeling empty when they ran out of things to say. With Mike Steen the words had to be right. Only she didn't know what the words would be.

Lory removed the bread from her mouth but didn't blink. The bone-deep exhaustion that had made putting on her tennis shoes an impossible task slipped from her bones. She felt thirteen years old simply because a hazel-eyed man was looking at her. Lory spoke first. "They told me one of the choppers was yours. I heard you a couple of times, but there was so much smoke...." She couldn't think of anything to say after that.

Without glancing at his fellow pilots, Mike dropped to his knees next to Lory and squared around so he could place his tray on his lap. "How long has this thing been burning?"

"We got here on Saturday. I don't know how long before that it started. A couple of days, I think." Discussing what brought them together was a safe subject. Why didn't it interest her?

"We better get it controlled damn soon. The weather isn't going to cooperate much longer."

"I know. Where . . . what have you been up to?"

Mike told her about the fires he'd been fighting for the past two weeks. She'd been in California while he was in Washington, then back in Oregon when he'd been called to Idaho. Ships in the night, she thought, but maybe they hadn't come that close. "I'm too tired to care," she admitted when he pointed out that she shouldn't be barefoot. "Its a bad summer. My folks are asking if I can come home soon. I don't know."

As Lory watched, Mike set down his barely touched dinner. "And your feet are killing you, right?"

Lory nodded.

"Maybe I can help." Slowly Mike cupped his hand around her right heel. Then he drew her leg toward him, his fingers already kneading her instep. Having his hand on her foot felt right, the best thing that had happened to her since they'd almost shared a kiss near a cafeteria door. "No blisters," he said. "Too bad. If you had some, you might get to rest tomorrow."

"Don't tempt me. Unfortunately I made sure my boots fit when I bought them." Without giving herself time to test the wisdom of what she was doing, Lory set aside her meal and leaned against her bedroll. Her eyes drooped and her lower jaw seemed incapable of staying in place, yet Lory was a long way from falling asleep. She was dimly aware of the other fire fighters watching Mike massage her foot, but she accepted their curiosity. Somehow Mike's fingers knew just where to press and where to apply a lighter touch.

Relief, slow and steady, worked its way into the bones of her feet. Drop by drop her exhaustion melted away and was replaced by an easy warmth. Although his hands went no higher than her ankles, Lory could feel the benefit of his massage climb to her calves, knees, thighs and beyond. Lory dropped her lids over her eyes, shutting out, she hoped, everything else she was feeling.

She was drifting, floating on a calm river with the sun's sensual fingers caressing her flesh. Only the heat she felt was coming from a man and not the sun, and the river she was floating on wouldn't have existed if anyone except Mike Steen had been touching her. Why she should be willing to let Mike dictate the ebb and flow of her emotions and why he out of the hundreds sharing the wilderness opening with them was capable of reaching her on this level she didn't know. Didn't care. Letting it happen was enough.

Mike tilted her foot upward and pressed firmly against the base of her toes, pushing out the effects of ten hours on her feet, replacing fatigue with energy. The energy was undeniably of a sensual nature.

With her teeth clamped over her lower lip, Lory opened her eyes. Mike was watching, eyes steady on her face and not the frail fabric that wasn't providing enough modesty. It was only when she glanced down at herself that Mike followed her lead.

"I had to have a shower," she explained. "I think I would have killed for one. But there's no privacy here. I didn't dare take off all my clothes. We...the women don't usually wear bras when they're fighting fire. Nylon can melt." She stopped. She should have never started on the subject.

"What you need—" Mike released her right foot only to pick up the left one "—is a luxury motel with hot water and a tub and scented bubble bath."

"Oh," Lory groaned. "Don't do this to me." If she lay back against her pack once again, Mike would know how much he was affecting her. But then he must know already. Lory let her head drop backward. "Don't spin me any fantasies unless you can deliver."

"When this fire's out."

"What's going to happen when this fire's out?"

"You're going to the best motel we can find and you're going to float in a tub until your skin wrinkles."

Lory laughed. She could hear amused chuckles from those she'd been sharing her meal with, but she didn't care. Mike's fantasy was too glorious to be ignored. "And how am I going to get to this motel? I came here in an army transport."

"We. I said we're going to find this here motel I've dreamed up. How do I know?" Mike's fingers were around her ankle but pushing against her pant leg, reaching for the tight swell of her calf. "We'll get a bullhorn and fly over the nearest city asking directions."

Lory lay still, waiting for Mike to continue his search, but her jeans had put an end to how high his hands could go up her leg. If they were in a motel and she wasn't wearing anything, this wouldn't happen.

"That's about enough daydreaming," Lory said shortly. She sat up quickly, the movement drawing her leg away from Mike. What she'd been thinking was definitely not good for her peace of mind. Mike was massaging her tired feet. He hadn't said anything about offering to share a bed. If she had the sense she was born with, she would find Ann and let the other woman's snores lull her to sleep. "We go back on the line at dawn. I need to climb into my bag and get some sleep."

"I'll help you." Mike tossed her her shoes and socks. While she shook pine needles off the socks and pulled them on, he gathered up her belongings. He was talking to the others now, answering questions about his chopper and asking if anyone knew how the California Angels had done on their last road trip. When Lory was finished tying her shoes, he helped her to her feet.

"My mother's an Angels fanatic," he told her. "It's embarrassing the way the woman carries on. I'm in hot water if I don't know how the team's doing," he explained as Lory led the way.

She tried to concentrate on what he was saying, but her senses were still reacting to his touch. Only the scattered beams of flashlights piercing the darkness of the area gave her any hint of where she should be going. But so what? She was operating on automatic pilot, anyway. In the forest her trained body did its job without being told. Tonight her feet were sure on the ground because her mind was filled with what she'd learned about what Mike Steen's touch could do to her.

In a few minutes Lory found where Ann had spread her sleeping bag. The other woman was a short distance away, sitting cross-legged on someone's sleeping bag while a group played cards. Ann called out to warn Lory that ants had been kicked up near a tree and that Lory would be wise to settle her belongings out in the open.

While Lory shook her sleeping bag out of its sack, Mike helped by emptying her backpack. "I've always wondered what fire fighters carried out onto the line." He held up three pairs of cotton socks, jerky, gloves, two wadded bandanas. When he came to a compactly folded bundle made of aluminum and fiberglass he frowned.

"Open it up," Lory offered without giving herself time to consider what she was doing. "That's what we call our brown-and-serve bag."

A minute later Mike had shaken the three pounds of material out until it formed a pup tent. He touched the outer aluminum layer. "It's fireproof. How do you use it?"

"I've never had to." Lory's eyes never wavered from what Mike was doing. "I pray I never have to."

Mike left the shelter he'd created to sit beside Lory on her sleeping bag. "Why?" he asked softly.

I'm not fooling him. He knows this upsets me. "That's— that's what we use when there's nothing else."

"When you can't get away from a fire?"

Lory shivered, barely remembering to nod. She hadn't wanted to let the emotion out, but she could smell the smoke sliding in from Saddle Mountain, hear the sounds of fire that were both a part of her makeup and the seeds of her nightmares. It had been night when Jeff died, when the danger in what she did for a living had blown up in her face. "Keith, my chief, he had to use one once. He said it was hell. I believe him."

Mike took Lory's strangely cold hand and folded it over his knee. He was watching her when he spoke. "Tell me what he said, Lory."

Mike was asking about Keith, but Jeff's memory wouldn't leave her alone. It had been a night much like tonight except that the wind had been stronger and the fire much closer. Heat, dry and alive with electricity, had swirled around the fire fighters. They had been working the night shift, light from the flames guiding them. *Stay here,* the crew chief had told them. But Jeff hadn't stayed. He'd walked out of her life.

Mike wanted to hear about the fire shelters. She could talk about that. "Keith was in Idaho. Out of Clearwater. They were fighting a firestorm. The winds had kicked up to where the wind was traveling faster than the flames. Before they knew it, Keith and the others were trapped." Lory moved her fingers restlessly under Mike's hand but didn't try to draw away. *Come back, Jeff,* she'd yelled at him, but he hadn't heard. Or hadn't listened.

"They couldn't get out of the way?" Mike prompted.

Lory shook her heavy head. Jeff had been dead a year and still she could hear herself screaming at him. It was so damn hard to talk about something else. "You've seen a fire-storm," she made herself say. "Separate fires coming to-gether and creating their own wind. Keith said that at the worst it sounded like freight trains passing overhead. The ground shook. The wind almost pulled the shelters off them." Lory couldn't take her eyes off the flimsy-looking tent. If Jeff had used his he'd be alive.

"And Keith still fights fires?" Mike asked. *What in God's name was going on here?* Lory was trapped in a nightmare that existed only in her mind. He wasn't sure he could reach her, but he had to try to bring her back to safety. He was asking questions because somewhere in her reply might be the explanation for her frozen fingers.

Lory nodded. She was afraid to lean against Mike, afraid she might expose too much of herself, open a door that couldn't be closed again. Keith's hell had been inside a fire shelter with red-hot walls sagging against him and dirt in his nostrils and his own screams tearing at his throat. Her hell came back every time she woke with Jeff's name on her lips and his form disappearing into the forest. "Keith says he's been through the worst. After that he can handle any-thing."

"What about you, Lory? What can you handle?"

What a fool she was to think she could keep anything from Mike. A woman who shivered and couldn't keep the blood running in her fingers was exposing a great deal. "I go on fighting fires," she answered simply.

"Just like Keith. Your reaction just now—you weren't reacting only to what happened to Keith, were you?"

"No." Did Mike Steen deserve more than that? No mat-ter—she couldn't give it to him. No one, not even her fam-ily, knew what she'd been through.

"Tell me about it, Lory." With his free hand Mike caressed the back of her neck. He knew he wasn't an expert on what it took to bring out the deepest human emotions, but when his grandmother had died he'd held his mother and that had helped both of them. Touching Lory was the only kind of communication he could give her.

Lory's sigh was too close to a whimper, but she held herself in check. Mike wasn't the only one who'd tried to get her to talk about Jeff's last night. Keith had been there. And Boyd and Ann, but none of them had pressured her like this. Although she was reacting to Mike's concern in a way she barely understood, that didn't make it any easier. "It's history, Mike. Let it go."

He had to accept her wishes. Someday, if he got to know her better, the barriers might drop away. But if he pushed things now she would only retreat. That was the last thing he wanted. He deliberately shifted the conversation in what he hoped was a safer direction. "Do you have to carry the fire shelter all the time? What if you're just mopping up?"

"We don't do much mopping up." Grateful for the change, Lory rolled her head, now fully aware of where Mike's hand rested. "That's one of the benefits of being hotshots. We don't have to do the scut work, the cold trailing and, yes, we always carry the shelters. Keith insists on it."

"Doesn't surprise me after what he's been through. I've never given the ground crew this much thought before," Mike admitted. "You have my utmost respect." Mike shifted positions, spreading his legs and pulling her against him, giving her his chest to rest her back against. When she readily accepted what he was giving her, he buried his nose in her hair and drank in the scent of her shampoo.

What they were doing wasn't safe. Even with the others around, it wouldn't take much for him to slide his hands to her breasts, to tip his head so he could run his lips over the long column of her neck. To change things between them.

"Just send money. Big bills. I'm sorry," Lory said so softly that the last two words were little more than a sigh. "Poor joke. Talk to me in the morning. Maybe I'll be coherent by then."

"I don't know if I'll see you in the morning," Mike pointed out, although that wasn't what he wanted to say. "Unless it starts raining tonight, which it isn't going to, we're both going to be at work before it gets light. Who do we talk to about the work schedule? I want Wednesday off so I can go golfing." Almost without his mind being in on the decision making, Mike's arms wrapped themselves around Lory's shoulders, pulling her even closer to him. Under his fingers he found the tempo of her pulse. Her back against his chest gave out a fragile warmth. If he told her what he was thinking, she might take her warmth away from him. What he wanted was to take this delicate woman and spirit her away from the dangers and challenges she exposed herself to every day. Just once she should know what it was like to let someone else take care of her.

"What we're going to get is lightning, not rain." Lory didn't try to keep the conversation going after that. Mike's massage had done wonderful things to her aching legs. His chest was the warm strength her tired body needed. She could, she admitted, if only to herself, spend the rest of her life next to him. His arms were warm blankets. Protection against the world.

But not protection against what she was feeling. Tired as she was, Lory would never be able to fall asleep as long as Mike Steen was sheltering her. The man who safely handled a massive helicopter through the fire-filled skies was also capable of great tenderness. He wasn't holding her simply to support her tired body. He wanted to feel her close to him.

She wanted the same thing.

For several minutes Lory thought of very little except the things she was learning about Mike Steen. Someone had turned on a radio in one of the forest service vehicles. An all-music FM station was playing peace ballads from the 1960s. The stark, clear voice of a woman who'd made a name for herself protesting war cut a swath through the reality of why all of them were here tonight. Lory was no longer the practical realist who depended on no one except herself. She was suspended somewhere between childhood and adulthood, a girl exploring what the word woman could mean.

Even when Mike's fingers left her collarbone and started downward, Lory felt no need to retreat from what they were sharing. He'd found the beginning swell of her breasts beneath her limp shirt and had spread his fingers over the soft flesh. Lory waited, not breathing, for him to test the boundaries of their relationship. To her relief he went no further. It was too soon. Neither of them was ready for anything more to happen.

Mike felt warmth and life in the woman who'd spent the past two weeks tiptoeing around the edge of his consciousness. Every time thoughts of her had threatened to surface, he'd pushed them aside, certain that she couldn't possibly mean more to him than any other woman ever had. But now that he was holding her in his arms, providing her with the strength she needed tonight, he was forced to face something in himself.

Lory was different. Why and how much he could only begin to understand. Mike tilted his head to the left, speaking into her ear. "I've been thinking, trying to remember when the last time was that I just sat and enjoyed my surroundings and who I was with. I'm glad this is happening."

"I thought about you the past couple of weeks."

"I've been thinking about you." Mike brushed his lips across the hair that fell over her ear. "Wondering if you were thinking about me."

Lory laughed. "We were obviously on each other's mind." She wasn't sure how Mike would take her deliberate attempt at a light touch, but it was necessary for her emotional security. There were risks in getting too close to someone else. Already she felt more attuned to Mike than those she'd been fighting fires with for years. The emotion was something she didn't know what to do with. "How does that singer hit those notes? I don't even like to listen to myself in the shower. Someday," Lory went on, "someday I'd like to have an expensive stereo system set up so—" Mike moved his fingers a fraction of an inch, and Lory forgot what she was going to say. The touch was intimate and yet chaste, whispers of warmth over her heart. Those whispers were making their impact felt throughout her body.

Lory pushed her head back, not to give Mike further access to her, but because her lungs craved more air. Had he moved his fingers because he didn't want to hear about stereos, or was he testing the limits of his impact on her?

She was telling him a great deal, more than she wanted to really, and yet the pure sensual pleasure of responding to his touch was worth the risk. How much more might be given and taken and exposed if they were alone left her shaken. Still, despite the risk, Lory closed her eyes, leaving herself free to explore the things he was showing her about her body. His hard inner thighs grazed against her. His chest formed the pillow for her head. She was closed in against him, surrounded by him, wanting everything he had to offer.

"Lory?" he whispered. Once again his breath feathered its way into her senses.

"What?" Was that her voice?

"I'm not sure this is wise."

Because her mind was on sensation and nothing else, it was a moment before Lory acknowledged that something was being asked of her. Why wasn't it possible to continue to float in this wonderful new world he was creating for her? "I'm not going to fall asleep if that's what you're thinking about," she said at last.

His lips were on her neck. Pinpricks of heat chased one another down her body and welled up inside her. She was a tinder-dry forest being touched by fire.

"I didn't think you were," he said finally. "It's going to be a long time before I can fall asleep tonight, Lory. That's the kind of impact you're having on me. We're playing with fire."

Don't. Please. Give me tonight. I'll deal with reality in the morning. But Mike was right. It was a simple matter of bodies too close together and hormones being given free rein. Physical attraction had its place, but they were mature adults beyond playing dangerous games. Biting down a sigh that said more than she was willing to expose or admit, Lory leaned forward and pulled herself out of Mike's arms. Then she pushed herself to her feet and stood looking down at him. "You're right," she made herself say. "It's that singer. That and stars and not enough sleep."

Mike continued to look up at her, his eyes exposing the lies. What he said, however, continued the lies. "You look exhausted. I'm feeling damn protective tonight."

"Oh," Lory whispered. The word sounded horribly inadequate.

"You need your sleep."

As if she'd be able to fall asleep, Lory thought, but she knew what was expected of her. "So do you." She smiled down at him and held out her hand to help him to his feet. His weight was almost enough to throw her off balance. Once he was standing, Mike was so close that words once again deserted her. Beyond all reason, the only thing Lory wanted out of life was to feel Mike Steen's lips on hers.

A trio of men walked by with empty canteens as they headed for one of the water trucks. Lory waited until they were gone before trying to take a backward step. Mike wouldn't let her.

His hands on her cheeks were strong and rough, a man's hands. Lory swayed slightly in reaction. When she lifted her head, her lips were parted. Slowly, asking permission with the measured movement, Mike covered them with his own. They came together, stopping only when Lory's breasts made the first gentle contact with his chest. With her eyes closed, Lory reached out until she found Mike's arms.

All first kisses should be like this, Lory thought as the female singer with her crystalline voice called out a haunting prayer for human understanding. What did it matter who might see her kissing Mike Steen? They were adults. Free. Without emotional ties to someone else. And if their ties to each other had no more substance than the night air, Lory would deal with that reality tomorrow.

She longed to press herself more tightly against Mike's strength and yet this fragile kiss demanded its own time. Her breasts were responding to the breathlike contact with his chest; they had to be giving out a signal he would understand. Was he ready to accept what she was giving?

Lord, she was beautiful. Mike accepted without question his reaction to a woman who cared little about what she wore or whether she had on makeup. She was intellect and commitment. She was the most wonderful, exciting woman he'd ever known. And yet, despite the fast cadence of his heart, he did no more than move his lips gently against hers.

"We might not be here after tomorrow," he whispered. He was testing the new emotional boundaries, playing with words to see if he could find the right ones.

"I hope so. I'm so tired." Physically tired, yes. But inside, where things were happening that had never happened before, Lory was awake in a new and exciting way.

Mike's hands were still on her cheeks. When he spoke, his lips were so close that it was all she could do to keep from covering them with her own.

"I really would like us to have some time once this is over. You can get away for a day or two, can't you?" he asked.

"I'm not sure. It depends on where they want us to go next." Why was she shaking? It wasn't cold.

"Find the time, Lory. Please. I want—I'd like to take you up in the Sikorsky."

"I'd like that."

"That isn't the only thing." The murmured words touched her lips, reminding her anew of how incredibly soft his mouth was. "You need to be pampered. I'd like to be the one to give you that."

"I don't—"

Mike covered her mouth with a weathered finger. "Don't, Lory. Just once let someone pamper you."

He was once again spinning a fantasy that Lory had dismissed earlier. Only this time she wasn't so sure it was a fantasy. "A motel?"

"Not just a motel. I want to give you luxury."

Lory gripped his elbows with new strength, waiting until his eyes locked with hers. He was spinning a dangerous dream. She wasn't sure she was ready for that. She also knew the personal cost if she turned him down. "A motel?" she repeated.

"Don't read more than that into it," he told her. "Lory, I want to give you something. I'm not going to ask for more than either of us is ready for."

"Thank you, Mike," Lory whispered. "I believe you."

Chapter Four

"Why don't they ever have ice cream at these centers? I've half a mind to call the President and complain. After all we do—"

Lory yanked off her backpack and laughed at her co-worker's ranting. "Didn't your mother tell you anything about nutrition? A man can't live by ice cream alone."

"Says who? I've been stuck in this damn place risking my neck for—" Bewilderment further clouded Boyd's sooty face. "How long have we been here, anyway? The least they could do is come up with something other than butter sandwiches. What are we, uncivilized?"

"Hey." Lory held up a hand in an effort to stop Boyd. "We'll be getting out of here." She shifted position in the back of the government-green pickup they were riding in, surrendering to the twin emotions of exhaustion and contentment. "Soon, my dear boy."

"It can't be soon enough for me." Boyd too shifted position, wincing as metal and his rear end made contact. "This has been one of the longest weeks of my life."

"I won't argue the point." Dust billowing up from the four-wheel drive's tires was reaching the truck's bed, but Lory was beyond trying to escape it. It had taken another twelve-hour day, but at last the word had gone out. The efforts of close to a hundred fire fighters, machinery and air support, plus a drop in the wind had done the job. The Saddle Mountain fire was eighty-percent contained. How could she feel anything but good? "What state are we in, anyway?"

"Florida. You'd never know it from looking, but we're on our way to the beach. Hot white sand, waves, sea gulls, girls in bikinis."

"You've been out in the heat too long." Lory held her handkerchief over her mouth and lifted her head over the side of the truck as if searching for Boyd's fantasy. They were heading down a steep, narrow logging road with evergreens growing close enough to reach out and touch. Lory wasn't joking. She couldn't remember which state they were in—only the man who might or might not be waiting at the end of the road. "Did you get hold of Sal last night?" she asked.

Boyd shook his head. "Thank God we're done here. I'm getting out of this hole first thing in the morning. I don't give a you know what if I have to hitchhike. I'm going to see my woman."

My woman. What would it feel like to be someone's woman? "What if we're sent somewhere else tomorrow?"

"Then they'll have to mark me AWOL. I ain't going. They wouldn't do that, would they?"

Lory hoped not, but this summer was a bad one. She might be crawling on hands and knees by the end of it, but at least her bank account would be healthy. "I'll put in the word for you at the weather service. Tell them no more lightning strikes until Boyd Doughtery has—what was that you and Sal are going to do? Build sand castles on this here Florida beach you've dreamed up?"

"If you don't know better than that, you have no business hooking up with this helicopter pilot of yours."

"He isn't my helicopter pilot."

"He could be. It sure isn't taking the two of you any time."

Lory knew better. Boyd had just opened up a hole large enough to drive a truck through. Still, Lory bit. "What isn't taking us any time?"

Boyd rolled his bloodshot eyes. "Getting to know each other." He turned toward another fire fighter who was in danger of collapsing against him and gave him a halfhearted shove. "What do you think, Randy? Think we ought to grill this joker, make sure he's good enough for Lory?"

"You characters stay out of this," Lory warned. The married men had teased her unmercifully about depriving the single men of the world of female companionship when there was no one in her life. Now it was obvious that they were going to tease her even more because there might be someone. "I don't need your help." She grabbed the side of the truck, trying, unsuccessfully, to ease the punishment to her rear end as the truck went through a dry creek bed.

"What do you know about it?" Boyd countered. "Where were you when they taught Dating 101? Someone with as much going for her as you do should be filling out joint tax returns by now. Either that or burning her bra at some women's lib rally."

"No one burns her bra anymore. If you'd spend some time reading the paper instead of chasing Sal around a beach, you'd know that." Lory felt good. Wonderful. Despite bumps and bruises and aching feet and a cotton-packed throat, they'd scored a victory today. Turned an angry devil into a caged beast.

And Mike would—maybe—be there tonight.

Boyd had gone back to talking about his wife and the fanciful trip they were going to take to Florida. He wasn't sure whether Sal wanted to pit her pregnant body against nubile coeds, but if she wanted to spend the time in their motel room, that was all right with him. Lory risked giving

Boyd a smile that went deeper than any words she'd ever said to him.

She envied Boyd and Sal, envied their marriage and love and the baby on the way.

"What do you want? A boy or a girl?" Lory asked when she could get a word in edgewise.

"Healthy." Boyd breathed deeply. "I want it healthy. Do you think it's too late to put in an order for twins?"

"I wouldn't," Lory warned. "Not if you want to keep your happy home."

Before her rear end turned black and blue, the pickup carrying a dozen fire fighters broke through the trees and into the fire's command center. Lory accepted the helping hands that eased her beaten body out of the truck, and she slung her backpack over her shoulder. "I wouldn't try to get between me and the water truck if I were you," she warned the others. "A woman deprived of a shower is a dangerous creature."

"You're in a good mood," Ann offered as the two women fell into step.

"The fire's contained. I can sleep for a hundred hours if I want," Lory said by way of explanation.

"It wouldn't have anything to do with a motel with a spa and hot tub, would it?"

Lory blinked. Ann hadn't been around when Mike was spinning his fantasy, had she? And even if she had, Lory didn't remember anything being said about spas and hot tubs. But in the closed community of fire fighters, nothing was sacred. "That does sound like heaven," Lory admitted. "However, I'll settle for cold water from the back of the truck and a bottle of shampoo."

"You've got be kidding! The man was serious. Don't let him back out of it now."

"Ann!" Lory stopped halfway through her warning. Carrying Mike's last words with her had kept her sane for the past twelve hours. She could keep her reaction to herself, or she could share it with Ann. "Have you ever done anything like that?" she asked. "Gone somewhere with a man?"

Ann stopped. Her own backpack was hanging limply from her large fingers. "Only with my husband," she answered softly. "I'm not the kind of woman men ask when they're looking for a hot weekend. You want the truth? I was lucky to have a half-dozen dates in high school. I remember listening to other girls talking about spending the weekend at Lake Tahoe, a summer romance at some resort where they were working. It didn't happen for me."

Lory didn't know what to say. She'd always thought of Ann as strong and competent and self-contained. But just because Ann could out arm-wrestle half the men here, didn't mean there weren't times when she wanted to experience fantasy. "I don't know," Lory finally admitted in a whisper. "I'd love to go—don't get me wrong—but there's more to it than that. I mean, I was raised believing that nice girls didn't."

"Nice girls do."

"I know that. Now. But, Ann, whether I spent a weekend with a man or not never meant much one way or another. I could always turn down the invitation and feel I'd done what was right for me."

"What about this time?"

"I don't know." The straps of Lory's backpack were cutting into her fingers, but she was only vaguely aware of the discomfort. "That's the hell of it. I don't know. This feels—different."

An hour later Lory wasn't any closer to an answer. After showering and exchanging boots for tennis shoes, the members of Keith's hotshot crew grabbed something to eat and then met around their boss's sleeping bag. There were a couple of small fires in the next county, but Keith had begged off for his crew. "My advice is for all of you to get out of here before someone snags us for another job. Lose yourselves for a couple of days and then get back in touch with me," he wound up.

Lory barely heard her foreman's advice. It was past dark. Surely Mike wouldn't still be in the air. Maybe he'd had second thoughts about last night's offer, and maybe it hadn't been an offer at all. Was she a fool for taking his talk about motels with endless hot water and trying to spin it into reality? Boyd was already trying to catch a ride with someone who would take him to an airport and home. Ann wasn't sure, but she thought her husband was on a run in this corner of Idaho. There were a couple of places she could call to try to hook up with him. The single men on the hotshot crew were talking about riding into the nearest town where the bars were jumping and the beer cold. Would Lory be the only one left alone?

When Keith was finished with them, Lory got to her feet and trudged back to where she'd left her belongings. If there were stars out tonight, they were being covered by billowing smoke rising into the heavens. Still, flashlights and lanterns and headlights cut through the night.

Suddenly Lory was seized with an overwhelming need to be alone. She'd been working shoulder to shoulder with others for almost a week now. They knew what she wore to bed, what color socks she pulled on in the morning, into which pocket she shoved a spare handkerchief. Last night a man had offered her escape from the world she'd chosen; tonight he wasn't here and she didn't know what to do with herself.

It was crazy. A minute ago her intention had been to stretch out on her sleeping bag, but that was before restlessness had washed over her. Her skin was too small; her thoughts too large. She hadn't felt this way since she was sixteen and filled with an energy without form or name. The only way she had of dealing with that energy was to start walking, start looking for solitude.

Lory had left the circle and was striding, hands jammed into rear pockets, toward a small, summer-warmed pool when she heard the sound. The helicopters were landing.

Would she expose too much of her emotions if she ran over to the Sikorsky? Would she be able to face the lonely consequences if she stayed where she was?

MIKE TOUCHED DOWN, shut off the engine and waited for the blades to stop rotating. Only a damn fool would have stayed out past dark, but whoever was deploying the choppers obviously didn't know enough about what he was doing. If it had been any other time, Mike would have jumped out and given the dispatcher a piece of his mind. But something more important filled his mind. He'd promised Lory Foster that he'd take her away from here.

If he could find her.

The night mop-up crew was out on the fire line, but the clearing was once again a sea of humanity. Tonight the din had a spark that had been missing earlier. In less than a minute, Mike became part of that energy. Together they'd licked the monster. This fire would soon be history.

"You ever go elk hunting?" one of the other chopper pilots asked as he caught up with Mike. "My brother went not far from here a couple of years ago. Said there were all kinds of cows, but they didn't see a single bull."

"I don't hunt," Mike replied. "That's something I never got into. I'd rather take pictures of wildlife than shoot them."

"You have something against hunting?"

Mike had a stock answer for the calmly asked question. "The way I figure it, if I keep on taking pictures, by the time I'm too old to do what I'm doing now, I can turn around and sell what I have to outdoor magazines. It beats sitting in a rocker."

The other pilot mulled that over while the two stood watching the activity beyond them. "How do you know when you're too old to fly?" he finally asked.

"I've got that figured out." Mike nodded somberly. "When I can't remember whether I'm going up or coming down, it's time to pack it in."

"Sounds good to me. Speaking of packing it in—" Grunting, the other pilot started toward the makeshift eating area.

Mike started to follow suit. He was still working the kinks out of his knees when realization struck him. Lory was out there, waiting. He made a ninety-degree turn and headed straight for her, although there was nothing but the sensation of deep, dark eyes on him to go by.

What was it he had said last night? That he wanted to take her out of this primitive place. They'd talked about a motel with endless hot water, or rather he'd talked and her eyes had said that she'd give a year of her life for that kind of luxury. She'd asked him if there was going to be more to the experience than a brief rest, but neither of them had come up with an answer.

"We did it," Mike said a few minutes later when he found Lory. She was standing with her back to the trees, her small face framed by untamed hair, body encased in jeans incapable of hiding her femininity. Mike couldn't breathe. "We licked that damn thing."

"Finally. Wasn't it dangerous for you to be out there after dark?"

"Yeah, it was." Mike glanced back at the helicopter, not trusting himself to speak until the spell she'd cast had been broken. "However, try to tell that to the powers that be. Just because I can fly Igor after dark doesn't mean I can fight fires then."

"Igor?"

"My chopper." This wasn't what he wanted to be talking about. Lory was standing toe-to-toe with him, arms hanging loosely at her side when they should be reaching for his neck. "Have you eaten yet?"

Lory nodded. "How about you?"

"Not yet. Will you join me?"

Five minutes later Mike was sitting cross-legged on the ground with Lory across from him. After recapping the day's activities, he couldn't think of a thing to say to her. If he didn't come up with something soon, she would grow tired of watching him try to swallow his cold meal and go in search of more stimulating conversation. He'd debated putting his arm around her shoulder or wrapping her tight against him while they waited in line. In the end, he hadn't done either, and now not even their knees were touching.

Any moment she would take her eyes off him and start looking around. "So what happens now? What do you have to do next?" he asked to forestall the inevitable.

"Nothing. I mean, Keith told us to take a couple of days off. If a call comes in, he doesn't want to be able to find any of us."

"So—what are you going to do?"

"I don't know."

Say it, Steen. The worst she can do is tell you to take a flying leap. "We aren't that far from Idaho Falls."

"Oh."

"I mean, if you're still interested in the offer I made last night, we could be there in about an hour." Mike sucked in his breath; he felt oxygen-starved.

Lory was staring at her tennis shoes. She'd picked up the end of one lace and was idly trying to poke it through the eyelet. "You really can fly at night?"

"We could leave Igor at the airport and rent a car. What is this? Wednesday? Thursday? The motels wouldn't be filled up, would they?"

"I don't think so."

Damn. Thirty-four-year-old men were supposed to know enough about women to know whether the woman was interested in what the man had to offer or not. But Mike had spent too much of his life alone in the air and not enough of it in the company of others. "Well?"

"Well, what?" Now Lory was twirling the end of the lace as tight as it would go and then releasing it. She repeated the movement.

"Do you want to go?"

"Yes."

"Yes?"

"Mike." Lory brought her eyes up from what her hands were doing. Mike wasn't ready for the uncertainty he found in their depths. "I don't want...I'm not ready for anything to happen."

Nodding like a wise man, but feeling like an idiot, Mike could only say, "I understand."

"Do you really?"

"Yes." His voice was firmer now. "We're friends. That's all it has to be."

If Mike ate any more after that, he wasn't aware. For a few moments they were both silent. Then he started talking nonsense, telling her about the time he'd been stuck in Idaho Falls for three days during a snowstorm. He'd bought a cheap sled and joined the youngsters taking advantage of the cancellation of school. No one, he told Lory, knew who he was or where he'd come from. He was simply Mike, the big stranger who could be conned into pulling endless sleds back up the residential streets.

"I'd like to do that again," he said as they collected Lory's belongings. "The little boy inside me didn't get his fill. There's something appealing about a snowstorm. There aren't any clocks to punch. No one gives a darn whether anything gets accomplished.''

"Hot chocolate."

"What does hot chocolate have to do with this?" Mike took Lory's backpack, sleeping bag and duffel and threw them into the back of the Sikorsky.

"Someone has to make hot chocolate."

"I forgot about that." Lory wasn't going to be able to get into the chopper without assistance. He'd helped any number of children climb in; this shouldn't be any more complicated. "All right. I'll amend that. Nothing has to be done during a snowstorm except making hot chocolate. Are you ready?"

Lory had been studying the helicopter's interior through the Plexiglas. She felt a childlike thrill in anticipation of lifting off and leaving Saddle Mountain behind. And yet more than the flight was framing her mood. What had she told Ann? That she'd never gone off with a man before. She didn't know any of the guidelines. No wonder she was scared. Or at least she told herself it was fear she was experiencing. "Ready," she whispered, reaching for the sides of the door, accepting Mike's hands around her waist.

She felt small. Fragile. Cared for.

Before Mike could climb into his side of the chopper, Keith stopped him. The crew foreman glanced in at Lory before squaring around to face Mike. "You work fast," he said.

"I'm not working anything." Mike bit down on anything else he might have said. Keith was Lory's boss, but that was all he was. He'd given her permission to leave. What she did on her own time was none of his business.

"Maybe. And maybe not."

If Keith was pushing, Mike would push back. "Lory needs a break. She needs to remember what it feels like to be a woman," he pointed out. "I'm sorry if you don't understand that."

"Oh, I understand all right." Keith blinked. When he opened his eyes, Mike read concern. "Look, I'd be the last one to stop Lory from enjoying herself," Keith continued. "She needs a life beyond work and family. I just don't want her to get hurt."

Hadn't Boyd said much the same thing the other day? But if the men weren't going to spell it out... "I'm not going to hurt her. Do you want to come along to make sure?"

"No, I don't want to come along. Look—" Keith raked a blistered hand through his tangled hair "—I'm not saying this right, am I? I'm glad Lory isn't going to be alone. She deserves something like this. It's just that, well, that woman in there is special. She went through a rough period last year. I don't want to see her hurt again. Keep that in mind, will you?"

How could he do otherwise? Mike wondered as he made a final check of the small tail rotor. It wouldn't surprise him to find Keith and Boyd demanding a blow-by-blow once the trip was over. But what they didn't understand was that Mike didn't know anything about whatever it was Lory had gone through. And he didn't know her well enough to ask.

"What do I do now?" Lory asked once Mike was seated beside her. Taking his cue, she was already reaching for her seat belt.

"You've already done it." Although he'd locked Lory's door after helping her in, he reached over and checked it again. The contact between his arm and Lory's ribs caught her unawares. She hadn't felt this nervous about a flight since her rookie summer. "Have you ever flown in a helicopter before?" he asked.

"A few times. But they've always been those big transport things." She would have liked to say more, but Lory was fascinated by the mechanics of bringing the helicopter to life. The engine and rotating blades made less noise than she thought they would, but its shaking eagerness to leave earth was enough to suck her into the mood. During her earlier helicopter rides, she'd been stuck in the vehicle's belly with other smoke jumpers. Watching Mike's hands move with unconscious sureness over the controls, Lory believed she now knew what it took to make a winner on any racetrack. Mike knew Igor; the two were one. Igor wouldn't fail the man controlling the machine.

"This is going to shake more than you're probably used to," Mike explained. "If there was much of a wind tonight, we'd be fighting that."

Lory nodded but didn't feel compelled to speak. She could look out to the side and front, could feel the power rumbling up through her feet to consume her body. In that half second when she wasn't sure whether they'd left earth yet, Lory came to understand why Mike Steen flew a helicopter. This was strength and freedom. Challenge and promise.

If she hadn't been used to flying, Lory would have been gripping her seat. Mike's hands and feet were in constant motion, controlling altitude and direction, pitch and turn. But she trusted Mike; she was able to accept the swift assent. They were airborne!

Lory waited until they'd cleared the treetops before letting out her breath. "This is fantastic!" She was leaning forward, trying to make out the water truck, bulldozers, pickups. But it was dark; night had swallowed the world she knew. "You can make it do anything you want, can't you?"

"Tonight I can," Mike pointed out. "But try keeping Igor on track when a fire has kicked up the wind. Going over Niagara in a barrel is probably a good comparison."

"I'll take your word for it, thank you." Lory breathed deeply. "I feel free. So free it's scary."

"Are you scared?"

"Not that kind of scared," Lory amended. Because her emotions were too great to contain, she reached over and squeezed Mike's hand. "I'm afraid I'll never want to come down again. Has that ever happened to you? I mean, do you ever want to keep on climbing just to see if this thing can go into orbit?"

Despite the faint light coming from the instrument panel, Lory knew Mike was watching her. "I think the altitude's getting to you. Yeah." He turned serious. "I love flying. There's something about being where no one can get to me. What I said about things getting pretty rough sometimes, that doesn't bother me. Sometimes—you're right. Sometimes I don't want to come down."

Lory relaxed against her stiff-backed seat. It was too dark to be distracted by anything beyond the helicopter's cabin. Her stomach had been slow to catch up with their ascent, but now she was once again self-contained. Everything she needed in the world was in the flying machine working its way through the mountains. "I was thinking..." she started slowly. "I don't know what all the excitement about Prince Charming and his white charger was. If I'm going to be spirited off somewhere, I'd much rather do it in a helicopter. What did you call it?"

"Igor."

Lory wrinkled her nose. "That's not very romantic."

"Igor Sikorsky. One of the true pioneers of helicopter development. What better name is there for one of his progeny?"

It took close to an hour and a half to reach Idaho Falls, but Lory didn't mind. In that time she learned a great deal about what it took to keep a helicopter in flying condition, that it would be a long winter if Mike's mother's baseball team didn't make it to the World Series, how there was never enough time to turn the house Mike had bought into a home. His voice was soft, relaxed. Despite the hum coming from the rotating blade, Lory was able to absorb everything he was giving her of himself.

In turn, Lory gave a little of herself. She pointed out that she didn't go into hibernation after the fire season was over. Calling herself a specialist in public relations, Lory explained that when she wasn't fighting fires or dealing with arson, she was usually buried under mountains of information that came from those affected by the forest service. "My dad says I'm a middleman, kind of a buffer between conservation groups and logging interests. Sometimes fighting a fire is safer than jumping into the middle of those disputes."

"Do you enjoy what you do?"

"Usually. I see my job as finding a common meeting ground," Lory admitted. "But not tonight. Tonight I'm on vacation."

The idea of being on vacation had truly sunk in once they'd landed and Mike had rented a car. Now they were driving down one of the main thoroughfares trying to read motel signs. "This is decadent," Lory breathed as Mike pulled into a sprawling modern complex that advertised everything from cable TV to hot tubs. "I can't believe I was breathing in smoke a few hours ago."

"Any regrets? You don't want me to take you back?"

"No, I don't want to go back."

Lory was even more convinced that she was ready to explore this fantasy night for everything it had to offer when they were shown to the suite with its separate but connecting bedrooms. When she heard what it rented for, Lory had tried to pull Mike out the door, but he'd brushed her off. The motel had several private spas, a heated indoor swimming pool and next to that two saunas. Cost wasn't a consideration, Mike told her in no uncertain terms.

"Decadent," Lory repeated as she took stock of her room, which was decorated in muted shades of green. Her bathroom was twice the size of the one she had at home and came complete with complimentary shampoo and conditioner, hand cream, even a sample-sized cologne. Although she'd never been one for taking baths, Lory could see herself falling asleep in the large tub, especially if she filled it with the bath oil provided by the management. "I could definitely get used to this."

Mike was trying out her bed. He bounced up and down on it and then pulled back the leaf-green spread to reveal lime sheets. He leaned down to bury his fingers in the carpet's thick nap. "Now I know I have to do something about my place. It can't hold a candle to this."

I'd like to see your place, Lory thought. Instead she commented on the view of a city park from her window. Having Mike sitting on her bed unnerved her. It wasn't that she didn't want him there; what made her draw inside herself was the battle being waged, which if lost would make a lie of what she'd told him earlier. Distance would keep them from making a possibly fatal mistake; distance might be impossible. "Where's the swimming pool?" she asked. "I don't know if I have the energy for that tonight."

Mike flopped back onto the bed, but kept his boots off the spread. "You don't have to do anything you don't want to, Lory," he said softly. "That's what this is all about. I saw you eyeing the tub."

Yes. That was something she could do that would be safe. "Would you mind? I mean, you can go swimming if you want to."

"Maybe in the morning." Mike sat back up. Lory had seated herself in a chair near the window and was unlacing her shoes. He watched her every movement. "Do you know what I'd really like?"

Lory forced her fingers to keep working. Was this a horrible mistake? Mike had put out an incredible amount of money. Maybe he was, despite what he'd told her, expecting something in return. "What?"

"You can't guess? You're the one who got me thinking about hot chocolate."

"You want hot chocolate?"

"Not hot chocolate. But hot chocolate syrup poured over ice cream. I'll probably have to go somewhere for it, won't I?"

Lory waited until she'd tucked her socks in her shoes and shoved them under the chair. The little boy who'd been here during a three-day snowstorm was still very much alive. "You and Boyd," she laughed.

Mike stood up and reached into his back pocket for his keys. "You don't want any? With nuts and a cherry on top?"

The nuts and cherry held no appeal, but the thought of having something cold and soft sliding down her throat was too much to resist. "Actually I like strawberry. With real pieces of strawberry in it."

Her confession netted her a smart salute and the smile Mike must have worn while sledding down city streets with ten-year-olds. "Your wish is my command. Why don't you have that bath while I scout this city out?"

After Mike left, it took Lory a couple of minutes to propel herself out of the chair and into the bathroom. She was tired, but her thoughts more than her muscles kept her where she was. Mike Steen was strong, competent, brave and all business while flying his helicopter. Her first impression of him had been of a man who took calculated risks and knew exactly what he wanted out of life.

But that was before he'd told her about playing in the snow, and had hurried off in search of a hot fudge sundae.

What are you, Mike? Lory asked as the skin-softening oil spread over her dry flesh. *Is the real you a man or a boy?*

The answer came almost as soon as the question was asked. Mike Steen was a man. Her reactions to him made that perfectly clear.

By the time Mike returned, Lory had soaked, shampooed and rummaged around for a tank top and pair of sweatpants to wear. She wished she'd thought to bring shorts that could double as a swimsuit bottom, but she hadn't gone on this fire call with any inkling that she was going to wind up here.

"Your timing is perfect," Lory said as she opened the door and took the overflowing carton from Mike. Had he changed somehow while he was gone, or had it been her wanting him back that made the moment special? "I want you to know—" she dipped the plastic spoon into her dish and popped a cold bite into her mouth "—only strawberry ice cream could have gotten me out of that tub tonight."

Once again Mike settled himself on her bed. His spoon was poised over his calorie-laden concoction, but he wasn't eating. Instead he took in Lory's tousled hair, her sleek and shining shoulders. Steam from the bathroom had drifted into the bedroom; the air smelled of lotion and cologne. Lory's tank top was wrinkled, her sweatpants baggy. Small feet poked out from beneath the elastic bands around her ankles. He thought she might have put on a little makeup, but he wasn't sure.

She was the most beautiful woman he'd ever known.

"Is it all right?" he made himself ask.

"Is what all right?"

"The ice cream."

"Oh, yes." Lory slid gracefully into a chair and ran her bare feet over the rich carpet. "It tastes even better than it looks." She wasn't looking at the dish in her hand. "Where did you find it?"

He told her, not because he cared that she knew how he'd spent his time, but because the room was full of the smell of her. He nodded in the direction of the bathroom. "I thought you might fall asleep in there."

"I almost did." Lory took another bite. "What about you? Don't you want to take a bath?"

"Later." Mike remembered to focus on what he'd driven five miles to find. "I like your outfit."

"I figured you might say something." Lory wrinkled up her nose and caught the extra fleece around her thighs between her fingers. "Isn't this disgusting? I latched onto it after my youngest brother left it in the dryer too long. I just hope that man gets married before he ruins all his clothes." The bath had left Lory feeling somehow separated from her body, with her mind drifting off in a fluffy cloud. The cold ice cream was bringing her back to earth. At least Lory tried to convince herself that ice cream was responsible for her renewed alertness. "That kid!" she went on. "Mom's about to give up on him. She thought she raised all of us to be self-sufficient, but Brent's a lost cause."

"All of you? How many kids did your folks have?"

"Five. Me and four older brothers." Lory isolated a chunk of strawberry and crunched down on it. "I tried to tell my folks it wasn't fair. If they were only going to have one girl, the least they could have done was have me first."

Mike had kicked off his shoes while Lory was talking. Now he swung his legs onto the bed and scooted back until the headboard was supporting him. "What's it like having siblings?"

"You don't have any?" Lory tried not to think about the long legs and hard thighs resting on her bed. It was impossible.

Mike shook his head.

"What's it like not having any brothers or sisters?" Lory asked softly. "I don't know if I can tell you what it's like having four older brothers because you don't have anything to compare it to." She stopped for a moment, not sure she had any right to ask the rest. But she and Mike were here for more than a sauna and a good night's sleep. There were things they, maybe, needed to know about each other. "Did you ever wish it was more than just you and your parents?"

"It was just my mom and me."

How could she have slipped up like that? What was it Mike had said, that he didn't know whether his father was alive? "I'm sorry."

Mike ran his free hand down his thigh, freeing the fabric over his taut muscle. He'd started speaking before Lory could take her thoughts beyond his action. "Why? Because there was just my mom and me?"

"No," Lory hurried to explain. *Nice girls do,* Ann had said. "It's just that—well, your upbringing is none of my business."

"Yes, it is." With a movement so fluid that it was accomplished almost without sound, Mike flopped over onto his stomach and stretched out on the bed. He was facing Lory, propped on his elbows. Although he was still eating, he did it without taking his eyes from hers. "I have nothing to hide. My parents were married, if that's what you're thinking about."

"I wasn't. Honest," Lory replied when Mike continued to look at her. "Mike, you said something about your father earlier. You didn't know whether he was alive. I don't know what that feels like. I can't even guess what it would feel like not to know anything about my father."

Mike was smiling. "I haven't needed psychiatric help because of it."

"I'm glad." Lory returned the smile. Warmth. The man had so much warmth in him. Maybe more than even he was aware of. "Would you like a bite of this?" She held out her dish. "It's really good."

"No thanks. I'd like to explain. You don't mind, do you?" When she shook her head, Mike continued. "I've had people ask me what it's like to grow up without a father. I'm not the only kid who has gone through that, of course, but people seem surprised that I wound up in what they consider a masculine career when I didn't have a father figure."

"I didn't think about that," Lory admitted. What she had been thinking about had very little to do with Mike's formative years.

"If you'd met my mother, you'd understand. That woman can outwrestle half the men in this state. Lory?" Mike frowned. "How can I miss something I've never had? I didn't know there was any other way to grow up except the way I did. Does that make sense?"

Lory had to grip her chair to keep from getting to her feet. Her fingers ached with the desire to smooth away the intensity on Mike's face. To brush away the tight lines around his mouth. "I think so. I never really had a close girlfriend while I was growing up. I think, although I'd never tell them this, my brothers were my best friends. I didn't miss having a girlfriend because I didn't know what it felt like to have one."

"Exactly. I've never felt as if I'd lost something because my father wasn't around. There haven't been that many significant people in my life. Fortunately I haven't lost any of them."

"I'm glad for you." The words were inane, but Lory couldn't get anything else out. This wasn't what she wanted to talk to Mike about. Not yet.

"Have you?" Mike was asking softly. "Lost someone?"

Be honest. At least give him that. "Yes, I have, Mike."

"I'm sorry." Mike sat up. His legs were hanging over the foot of the bed. He could reach out and touch her. If he did, would his touch take her thoughts out of the past? "Was it someone in your family?"

Lory shook her head.

"Who?"

"He—" This wasn't what tonight was supposed to be about. Mike had promised her rest. A vacation. Her nerves were telling her that something entirely different was taking place. Either way, this wasn't the time to let the past intrude. "It was a long time ago, Mike."

"And you don't want to talk about it, do you?"

"No."

Chapter Five

Five minutes ago Lory wasn't sure she had the energy to climb into the hot tub connected to Mike's bathroom, but that was before the conversation skated too close to dangerous territory and Mike had brought her back from the edge. "I don't know how much time we're going to have," Mike had said. "I don't know about you, but I think we've done enough talking. Last one in the hot tub's a rotten egg."

Now, despite feeling foolish over her attire, Lory had slipped out of her sweatpants and was slowly lowering herself into the hot, bubbling water. "If only the guys could see me now," she muttered. "If I die tonight, at least I'll die happy."

"If what guys could see you?"

Lory wasn't ready to have Mike join her. He'd set the jets and heat for the hot tub and then disappeared into his bedroom. She'd hoped it would take Mike several minutes to change. She needed the time to convince herself that she'd actually agreed to share this small space with him, that the pull she'd felt while in her room wouldn't return.

She hadn't been given enough time. "The guys I work with," she answered after a hesitation that lasted too long. As Mike tested the water in the sunken tub with his toe, Lory looked up, watching. Somehow he had come up with a black bathing suit. Although it wasn't as skimpy as her under-pants, it didn't leave nearly enough to the imagination.

This was going to be hard, harder than anything she'd done in a long, long time. Ann was wrong. Going to a motel with a man, this man, wasn't a fantasy. It was reality. A fine mist of dark hair covered Mike's chest. The same soft curls ran down his thighs. She'd been in his arms—she knew he was strong—but feeling and seeing his muscles were two different things. His arms around her had been both comforting and something dangerous. Sitting in the hot tub with nothing to take her mind from the masculine form slowly joining her had her instantly on edge. There was only one thing she could say. "Where did you come up with a bathing suit?"

"In my duffel bag. I always carry one."

"I'll have to remember that. I feel pretty foolish." Although she was up to her neck in the hot tub, Lory picked at her wet, limp, sleeveless T-shirt. "Not exactly the outfit for this setting."

"Are you comfortable?"

Comfortable wasn't the operative word. It was impossible to be comfortable with a man's legs brushing hers while hot water swirled around them. "Yes," she lied.

"Then that's the most important thing." Mike found a spot to sit across from Lory and leaned back until his head was resting against the edge of the tub. He let his hands float to the surface. The tips of his fingers dangled a few inches from Lory's shoulders. "So this is how the rich and famous live. I could definitely grow to like it."

Don't touch me. Not yet. I need—time. She must have been a total idiot to second the suggestion that they finish their desserts and try the hot tub. At the time Lory had been interested in nothing more than putting an end to the dangerous direction the conversation had gone. Now she could feel Mike's presence throughout her body as the current bounced off him and entered her. If she moved her legs, she would find his. If she shifted position, her shoulders would come in contact with his fingers.

Only an idiot wouldn't acknowledge the position she'd placed herself in, and Lory wasn't an idiot. They were here because something that demanded exploration had come to life between them. The only question was, which of them would be the first to acknowledge it? "My folks are always saying they're going to do something like this," Lory said in an effort to get the conversation going. "Running their own business keeps them pretty tied down." Lory explained that in addition to the guide service, they rented out rafts that could be used on quiet stretches of the river and planned occasional fishing trips. During the winter, snowmobile rentals and expeditions paid the bills. "There's always something going on. It's hard for them to get away."

"What would they think if they knew where you were, Lory?"

It was an honest question. "It wouldn't bother them, if that's what you're thinking."

"That wasn't what I was thinking. You aren't a little girl anymore. It's your life. You can do whatever you want."

"As long as I'm willing to live with the consequences," Lory answered softly. "Are you asking whether they'd think this was wise?"

The fingers that had drifted so close to Lory's cheek finally made contact. Mike touched his fingertips to the warm flesh with a gesture that said he had no qualms about where the conversation was going. "I've never done this before, Lory. I wanted you to know that. I've never taken a woman to a motel."

"Is this what this is? A man has taken a woman to a motel?"

"Is that what you think it is?"

Lory took a deep breath. Despite the fingers on her cheek, she knew what her answer had to be. Not so much for Mike's sake, but for hers. The desire to let go was strong and real. Lory could give herself to Mike—they both wanted that—but tomorrow would have to be faced.

"That isn't the way it's going to be. Mike, I came with you for a lot of reasons." She had been pressing her hand against one of the jets, but now she brought it to the surface and took Mike's fingers. "I wanted all the things we talked about earlier. Time away from work. A chance to sleep in a real bed. I wanted to pamper myself and be pampered." Her grip strengthened. "I also wanted to get to know you better."

"Did that come first or last?"

The ripples of unease that had washed over her while she had waited for Mike to join her in the tub were no more. He believed in honesty. She could handle that. "First." A shy smile touched Lory's lips. "You're a fascinating man, Mike Steen. Getting to know you is a lot more important than..." She left the obvious unsaid.

"And you're a fascinating woman, Lory Foster."

"Now..." Lory paused. "Now that we've got that over with, what happens next?"

Mike slowly pulled his fingers free. He leaned forward and lightly covered Lory's shoulder with a hand strong enough to jockey a helicopter over the mountains. "That's for you to decide."

Even before the words were said, Lory had known that. She didn't mind being given the responsibility. Because she'd spent her working life surrounded by men, Lory knew the signs. Mike was sexually attracted to her. The emotion was returned. But just because Lory felt his touch on a level that went far deeper than her flesh didn't mean she was ready to jump into bed with him. "I like hearing you say that," she told him.

Mike withdrew his hand. His eyes stayed locked with hers. "What have you decided?"

"That I want to get to know you. That's all. I hate wrestling matches."

Nodding slowly, Mike brushed sweat off his forehead. "Then there won't be a wrestling match. So you want to get to know me. What's important? My mother's name is Nat. She was born a Natalie, but if you call her that, she'll never forgive you."

"What's your father's name?"

"Robert." Mike blinked but didn't try to break eye contact.

She'd said the right thing. She'd told him this wasn't going to be a one-night stand and he was still here. Wrapping her emotions around her, Lory concentrated as Mike continued.

"He was between jobs when my parents were married, but that didn't last long. He's an engineer specializing in the designing and building of bridges. He doesn't come cheap."

"His work takes him a lot of places?" Lory guessed.

"It doesn't have to. But that's what he wanted."

"Mike?" Lory hesitated. Her question wasn't easy; maybe Mike didn't want to answer. But she'd said she wanted to get to know him and he'd agreed. "Was he around at all when you were a child?"

"I wouldn't recognize my father if he walked in the door."

Lory tried to read bitterness and hatred into Mike's words, but the emotions weren't there. Still, sliding closer so that they were no longer sitting across from each other, she took his hand. "I can't imagine what that's like."

"And I can't imagine knowing the man. Life turns out differently for everyone, Lory." It was Mike's turn to close the gap between them even further. Lory felt his hip brush against hers and wondered at her ability to hold her reaction in check. After a minute he went on. "I told you, my mother's a teacher. She's part of a decent-sized district now, but when I was growing up we lived in a small town that depended on one lumber mill for its existence. My mother taught all eight grades."

"Why isn't she there anymore?"

"The mill closed down. The town dried up." Mike paused, wrapped his arm around Lory's shoulder and went on. "She was the only single woman in the town. The other women didn't quite know what to make of her and the men pretty much left her alone because they'd hear from their wives if they didn't."

Lory felt light-headed. Whether it was from the effects of the tub or empathy for Mike's mother or reaction to his touch, she didn't know. Maybe it was all three. "It must have been lonely for her."

"It was. I didn't know it at the time. I thought the town was a great place to grow up. It was safe—there wasn't anywhere I couldn't go. My mother's one of the most self-sufficient people I've ever known. There isn't much she won't tackle and not much she didn't expect her son to tackle."

"I believe it," Lory admitted. "I've seen the result."

"I owe it all to Mom. At least that's what she tells me." Mike laughed. The sound rumbled through Lory, both sensitizing and calming her. "There was none of that 'my little man' garbage. I was determined not to grow up a mama's boy, as if she'd let me. She called me a chip off the old block when I took over splitting wood for our heat."

"In other words," Lory guessed, "you were following her guidance."

"Exactly. If I can stand on my own two feet, it's because she was the role model I needed. Not only did she split wood, but she went out in the woods and chopped down the trees. What could I do?'' Mike laughed again. ''I couldn't let my mother show me up.''

As far as she knew, Lory's mother had never taken a chain saw or an ax to a tree, but with a husband and four sons, she didn't have to. Instead, Lory's mother taught her sons, as well as her daughter, to keep their clothes clean, use their brains and get themselves out of whatever scrapes they got into. Bloody noses, even her only daughter's bloody nose, didn't faze her. ''I think our mothers would like each other,'' Lory whispered. It was her turn. She should give him some idea of the forces that had shaped her.

But Lory had been awake since dawn, fought a fire, taken a helicopter to an airport and gone in search of a motel. She'd been asked to face her own sexuality, to deal with what she was feeling as best she could. The only thing she cared about was the impact the man holding her was making on her senses. ''What would your mother think if she could see us now?''

Mike's deep chuckle was yet another assault on Lory's nerves. ''She'd probably say she didn't know I could stay in one place this long, and that it was about time.''

Without missing a beat, Lory asked her dangerous question. ''That what was about time?''

''This.'' Mike turned Lory toward him so smoothly, so gently, that Lory didn't know she'd been lifted off her seat and onto his lap until his lips were too close to be denied. She acknowledged the undercurrent of bare flesh joining, separate pulses becoming a single beat. Lory did the only thing her tired mind wanted out of the night. She wrapped her arms around Mike's neck to steady herself and allowed the contact to be made.

Lory was flowing into Mike, losing touch with her separate identity. If either of them made a sound, she was unaware of it. Somewhere, coming from a source so deep that she was unable to isolate the sensation, she was aware of the gentle vibrations the bubbles were making, the numbing quality of the body-temperature water. And yet those things were nothing.

Mike's lips were everything.

Mike knew he was taking unfair advantage of the woman in his arms. Practiced as he was in gauging the strength of his helicopter, Mike was aware that Lory was on the raw edge of exhaustion. He correctly guessed that the hot tub had sapped her of the strength to do anything except surrender to him. He wondered if she would protest if he pulled the tired old T-shirt over her head, or if she was beyond making any decisions. He was tempted to test his theory, to carry her out of the tub, lower her onto his bed and let instinct take over.

But if he did that, Mike wouldn't be able to face either of them in the morning. And being with Lory Foster tomorrow, and other tomorrows, meant more than tonight's gratification. "I think you'd better get out of here," he whispered with his lips still against hers.

"Why?"

Don't ask me that, lady. Not while you're doing what you are to me. "Because you're going to fall asleep, and if you drown, the motel is going to be in a lot of trouble."

"I'm not going to drown." Lory tried to increase her grip on Mike's neck, but the strength had been stripped from her arms. "I've been swimming since I could walk."

"Are you sure you can walk?"

The question caught Lory unawares. She tried to concentrate on her legs, but they belonged to someone else, someone without nerves or will. She giggled when she noticed that they'd floated off Mike's lap and were dangling limply in the water. "I'm not sure of anything. Are you sure you didn't put something in my ice cream?"

Mike expected Lory to take over responsibility for her body at any minute, but until she did, he would have to do the work for her. He planted his feet under him, gripped her securely in his arms, and lifted both of them out of the water. He stood on the underwater seat until water was no longer streaming off them, then stepped out. "Are you suggesting I spiked your ice cream?"

"I guess not," Lory admitted. She should insist that Mike put her down. She was too heavy and wet to be carried into his bedroom. Yes, that's what she would say—in a minute. "I think the hot tub has stripped all the strength out of my body."

"And I think you're totally worn out." Mike dipped his head until his ear was close enough to Lory's breast that he thought he could hear her heart beating.

"Am I?" Lory muttered. They'd been comparing their mothers a few minutes ago. How had they gone from that to his holding her against his naked chest while they dripped on the new carpet?

"Yes, you are." He shouldn't have done it. Lory was vulnerable, and taking advantage of her vulnerability wasn't fair. But her lips were willing and soft, her body trusting against his.

God, she belonged in his arms! For the first time in his life, Mike felt ready to take physical responsibility for another person. He would pull back the coverlet, place her in his bed, slowly strip her clothes off her, take her breasts in his mouth and her body in his arms...

"Mike? I'm too heavy."

She wasn't, but because she had started to struggle, he let her down. As she planted her feet under her, Mike shook off whatever it was that had made him want to spend the rest of his life holding her. He was wrong; Lory Foster didn't need or want any man to take responsibility for her. Maybe, someday, they'd find a way to unite his wanting and her not needing, but this wasn't the time. "You're dripping."

"So are you."

"What do you think we ought to do about it?"

"Change?" Lory picked at her T-shirt, trying to lift it off her breasts. The top wasn't loose enough to accomplish that, and she let it continue to hug her.

"We haven't gone swimming yet," Mike teased to keep his mind off what was being revealed under the ridiculous old garment. "There probably isn't anyone in the pool this late."

"Tomorrow." Lory groaned. "Mike, I can't go wearing this."

Before she could pick at her T-shirt again, Mike turned away. He wondered how early the stores opened. Anything he bought for her had to be less of a threat to his self-control than what she was clad in now. "So you're not a fashion plate," he heard himself say. "You didn't hear me objecting, did you?"

"You didn't have any choice. You know what my wardrobe consists of."

Mike turned back. Lory was trying, with limited success, to pull her hair away from her neck. While they were in the water, he'd been unable to see what else she'd been wearing. The tiny strip of lilac lace underwear was the last thing he expected, given the jeans that were her uniform, and yet it was right. A woman who had just shaved her legs should be wearing something feminine. And yet, the femininity came from more than lilac and lace. Lory possessed an in-born grace, an easy acceptance of her body. Her almost perfect body held him spellbound.

"What are you looking at?"

Mike stiffened at the accusation in Lory's voice. He brought his eyes up. "That scar." Mike pointed at a thin white line running across Lory's kneecap. "Did you get that fighting fires?"

"That old thing?" Lory's laugh warmed him; she'd forgiven his staring at her. "I've had that since my high school days."

"Your brothers?"

"No. Not that they wouldn't like to take credit. I played on the girls' basketball and volleyball teams. I was good, too." Lory grinned boastfully. "Unfortunately, I didn't know enough to ride the bench long enough to let my knee heal after I twisted it. Finally a surgeon had to step in and do some repairs."

"It doesn't bother you anymore?"

Lory reached down and poked at her knee. "That's the end of my war story. I could tell you about hobbling around on crutches in a three-story school, but I won't bore you with the details."

How easy it was for Lory to dismiss the one flaw on her magnificent body. "Did you play after that?" he asked.

Lory gave up her study of the scar and went back to trying to dry her hair. Her movements were doing things to her breasts that were almost more than Mike could handle. Still, he concentrated on what she was saying. "You better believe it. State championship in basketball my senior year."

He had to say something. "And you were the star."

"Sure." Lory tapped herself on the shoulder, but her grin gave her away. "Actually, I was a bit player for this six-foot center we had. Reni got the scholarship, the newspaper headlines. Ah, well, it was a lot of fun while it lasted. Mike?"

"What?" Had he given himself away?

"I'm sorry. I'm out on my feet."

Of course she was. "Me, too," he lied, and let her go.

A minute later Lory was in her bathroom. She struggled out of her wet clothes and hung them over the bathtub to dry. Next she selected a large towel and dried herself. Finally she wrapped the towel around her hair and walked naked into her bedroom. She pulled an oversize man's shirt out of her duffel bag and slipped into it. The shirt was long enough to reach halfway down her thighs, and she convinced herself that the neckline wasn't low enough that it revealed more than it should.

Lory reached to turn off the bedroom light but stopped when she caught her reflection in the sliding glass door. The shirt disgusted her. What man would want anything to do with someone dressed like that? She had a few decent nightgowns at home, but they were hardly the sort of thing she could wear when sharing her sleeping space on the job with God knows how many men.

But tonight she was sharing sleeping space with only one man. Not that she wanted to wave an open invitation at Mike, but wasn't there a halfway mark? Some subtle indication that she thought of herself as a woman?

Lory walked back into the bathroom. She yanked off the towel and attacked her still-damp hair. She didn't stop brushing it until static electricity caused the strands to float around her cheeks.

"Better," Lory muttered once she was through. Maybe she wouldn't see Mike before she climbed into bed, but if she did, she'd done something to blunt the impact of the sad nightshirt. Her first reaction to seeing Mike staring at her legs had been irritation, or at least she'd thought that was what she was feeling. But she'd taken a long look at Mike while he was getting ready to join her in the hot tub. Didn't he have the same right?

It hadn't been irritation at all. Mike's appraisal of her had pushed her nerves into high gear.

Getting through whatever time they spent here without becoming lovers wasn't going to be easy. A man doesn't pull a woman onto his lap or hold her in his arms—or kiss her— if she means nothing to him. She had never felt this way about Boyd or Keith or anyone she worked with. Either of those men in the next room wouldn't have kept her from a good night's sleep.

Mike was different.

"Lory? Are you decent?"

Despite the softly spoken question, Lory jumped. Thinking about Mike and having him back in her bedroom were two distinctly different things. She wasn't at all sure about the sexlessness of what she was wearing. "What do you want?"

"Breakfast. To talk about breakfast, that is."

Lory breathed a sigh of relief. That was a safe subject. She could have told Mike that he could come in, but she walked over and opened the door. He was wearing pajama bottoms but was naked from the waist up. Like her, he'd dried his hair. And he'd shaved.

She felt the impact everywhere.

Given her four brothers and the way she earned her living, Lory had seen more men ready to go to bed than most women. But Mike's pajamas were riding low on his hips and his chest was giving off a warmth that drew her like a magnet. "What about breakfast?" she managed. Although Mike's arms were hanging at his side, his fingers had curled into fists. He was staring so resolutely at her face that it unnerved Lory. *He hates what I'm wearing. I look like a man.*

"What time do you usually get up?" he asked.

What time indeed? "Usually the sun gets me up. It's summer, so it'll be early. But you don't—"

"I need to run out to the airstrip first thing in the morning," Mike interrupted. "Igor needs a new rotor clutch. I need to call around and see if someone has one I can use."

A rotor clutch. That made no sense, but Lory wasn't interested in an explanation. "Take as long as you need to. You don't have to feel responsible for my breakfast."

"How about nine? That wouldn't be too late, would it?"

Breakfast at nine with Mike Steen. "That sounds fine." If he didn't take his threatening, exciting body out of her bedroom, Lory wasn't sure she could be responsible for what might happen next.

"All right. And after breakfast maybe we can go swimming."

"Swimming. That sounds fine."

"But first we're going to buy you a bathing suit."

"You don't—" Lory started and then gave up the pretense. She wasn't interested in talking. She was even less interested in a bathing suit. It was all she could do to keep her hands off him.

"Look, you're tired," Mike was saying. "You need to get some sleep."

"Yes. Yes, I do."

"Well—"

He should be saying good-night. He'd said everything he'd come in here to say. Why then was he taking another step toward her? Why was he cupping his hands around her cheeks and lifting her head? Asking. Claiming her.

Suddenly more awake than she'd been since she'd gotten up that morning, Lory leaned into Mike and wrapped her arms around his broad chest. Yes! Oh, yes. His lips were everything she'd remembered.

Although she had no thought of breaking the contact, Mike was still holding her head in place. His lips were sweet and warm; the warmth was the same as that leaving his chest and entering her. Lory allowed her lids to slide down over her eyes, wanting nothing of the room, the motel, the city they were in.

She wanted only one thing.

Mike was more aware than Lory of the danger inherent in their kiss. She might be taking their relationship one slow, wise step at a time. He, however, had spent too much time in a hot tub with a sensual, desirable woman. He'd tried a cold shower a few minutes ago, but all that had accomplished was to wash away the mantle of lethargy created by the tub. Now he was wide awake, and acutely aware of who he held in his arms.

No one, nothing, could reach them here. This was their time. Their exploration.

Lory gave so freely; her kiss held nothing back. How could she expect him to hold himself in check when he felt as if he were holding her heart in his hands? Mike ran his hands upward from her cheeks until he'd buried his fingers in her hair. The strands were soft and sleek, feathers of feeling touching nerves he'd never known his hands possessed. He found the pulse points at her temple and pressed the tips of his fingers against the faint throbbing until the beat became his.

His mouth hadn't left hers. As the seconds ticked off, their kiss became more, a deep journey destined to take him on roads he'd never traveled before.

Several years before, Mike had gone through his only dating frenzy. He'd just struck out on his own and that first winter there hadn't been much work. He'd filled the empty hours by going out with every woman who had shown the slightest interest in him. For the first few months he'd felt like a wolf let loose in a chicken coop. But then the faces had started to blur together. He could no longer put names to the voices on the phone. The women, without exception, had had the same impact on his ego. They had seen his life-style as the epitome of masculinity. He was someone they could look up to, someone to parade in front of their envious friends, someone to point to as one of the last examples of the meaning of the word macho.

Mike had quickly grown tired of the role he'd been asked to play. He had no use for women who melted in his arms. It was all too easy.

Tonight was different. The woman was different.

Mike's hands were on the move again. Although Lory's fingers were still pressing against his spine, he felt free to explore. Mike ran his hands down her neck, pausing to absorb the incredible softness he found. Her collarbone was sharply outlined, her shoulders a marriage of strength and silk. She quivered as he pushed her shapeless shirt away from her throat. When he lowered his head and covered her throat with his lips, her trembling deepened. It was happening so fast. Her response was so complete.

So was his.

His tongue entered the exploration, finding satisfaction in the moan that came up from her. Lory arched her spine backward, giving him access to the silken tanned flesh.

Growing bold with wanting, Mike dropped his hands to Lory's hips and slowly drew her nightshirt upward. Satin flesh awaited his touch. Lory's thighs and hips, like her shoulders, gave the double message of competence and femininity. She was small-boned and delicate, but that was only the surface message. Beneath the surface was a woman designed to master the life-style she'd taken on. He could drink in that strength, blend it with his. Make them one. The consequences of such total surrender entered his mind but were cast aside.

"Mike," Lory gasped. "Please—"

She wasn't going to ask him to stop, was she? Not now that the blood was pounding in his veins.

"I . . . we had an agreement."

"Lory?" God, he loved saying her name. "I think we both want this. I know I do."

Lory still had her hands knotted around his neck, yet she was trying to draw her body away from his. Under his touch, Mike felt goose bumps erupt on her thighs. "I don't want to be a one-night stand, Mike."

Mike had heard women tell him that before. Because he was a gentleman, he'd never pressed the point, but because the women in question seldom actually put on the brakes, he hadn't often had to deal with the reality of the words. That was before Lory.

"You aren't that." He hadn't been able to take his hands off her creamy flesh. Even as he spoke, he was pressing her hips toward him, letting her know what she was doing to him.

Lory froze. Being in Mike's arms, losing herself in his kiss had been right, she told herself. She'd even been able to justify his pushing aside of her nightshirt. What did she mean, justify? Her every thought, both conscious and sub-conscious, had followed what he was doing. But what he was showing her now, that was dangerous territory.

Dangerous for both of them.

"Mike. Don't," she warned. "I mean it."

"What do you mean?" Mike still had his hands on her naked hips, but he was no longer trying to hold her against him.

"It's too fast. At least it is for me. I won't be treated this way." Her anger was directed, not at him, but at the war within her. Was it so wrong for them to become lovers? Neither of them was attached. They felt—something—for each other.

But neither of them had asked for more than tonight. "I don't want it this way, Mike."

This time her words had the necessary effect. Slowly, like a man replacing a fragile vase on a shelf, Mike smoothed her nightshirt down over her thighs. "I won't push you, Lory."

"Mike, I'm not sure my coming here was a good idea." Where the strength to speak came from Lory didn't know.

Mike took a backward step. "At least you're honest."

She'd hurt him. That was the last thing she wanted to do. "Don't. Mike, please," she begged. Somehow her hands found his waist. She was gripping the loose elastic of his pajama bottoms as if that hold could keep him there. "I don't want to hurt your feelings."

"Didn't you?" Mike raked a hand through his hair, but didn't try to break free. "Forget that," he amended. "I'm sounding like a spoiled kid." He took a deep breath. "You have every right to say what you did."

"But that's not what I meant." Lory stopped, confused. A million thoughts were rampaging through her; she couldn't find the right words to explain any of them. She felt ridiculous trying to hold on to his pajamas, but was afraid she would draw more attention to what she was doing by letting go. "I'm glad I'm here. It's just that we haven't known each other very long," she tried to explain. "I have to stay in control of what I'm feeling."

"And what are you feeling?"

How could he ask her such an impossible question? "That—Mike, I'm attracted to you." Unaccountably Lory laughed. "That's obvious, isn't it? But I'm not that sure of my emotions. I . . . went through a bad experience last year. I'm not sure I have that behind me. Until I do, well, I have to take things slowly." What a pitiful explanation that was, and yet it was the best she could do.

"Then you aren't sorry you came here?"

"No. Oh, Mike, no!" Lory released Mike's waist and reached for his hands. Her first impulse was to press them against her breasts, but she fought that off. Instead she simply held on. "It's been perfect. The flight, the hot tub, everything." *And you. You're the most perfect thing.*

"I'm glad." Was Mike whispering, or was it only her imagination that made his voice sound weak? "Like I said—" he turned his hand around in Lory's until he was the one doing the holding, the lifting of her fingers to his mouth "—we'll have breakfast together."

AN HOUR LATER MIKE was standing in front of his window, staring out at city lights. He wondered if Lory was taking in the same view or if she'd been more successful at falling asleep.

Mike hated deep, painful pasts. It was his belief that the only thing a person could do was to live in the present. Past mistakes and triumphs had little to do with making today work. He wanted to shake Lory, to demand she get rid of whatever emotional baggage she was carrying around. But if he tried that, he'd wind up holding her against him, running his lips through her hair, asking her to give more than she'd given so far.

And he might wind up giving Lory Foster more than he'd ever given a woman before.

What was the matter with him? Except for that brief period when he'd run wild through the state's female population, he'd been a loner. Mike had a deep commitment to his mother, but she'd been the only one he'd ever felt that way about. Women were for conversation, making love to, sharing a transient experience with.

Sometimes, when he thought about not having anyone waiting for him when he came down out of the sky, Mike wondered if he had the capacity to love, but those thoughts didn't last long.

Mike believed in today. In what he did for a living. The future might never arrive. And the past, like his father, had no bearing on what he was today.

That was what he wanted Lory to understand, to believe.

Lory! He loved the sound of her name.

Chapter Six

When she woke a little after six the next morning, Lory heard Mike rummaging around in his room. Picturing his movements came as easily as breathing. His callused right hand was turning on the water in the shower. With his other hand, he unfastened the pajama bottoms. They slid off his rock-hard thighs, leaving him magnificently exposed. Lory's fingers twitched restlessly as she pictured him soaping his body, letting water cascade off his competent shoulders. Would he shave before dressing? Would he pause a moment to appraise his body, or was it so much a fabric of his being that he was able to dismiss what fascinated her?

Lory's first impulse was to let him know she was up. But by the time she heard the opening and closing of his dresser drawer, she'd thought better of her impulse. Mike hadn't invited her to join him. He was used to being alone.

So be it. Lory wasn't going to try to change Mike's nature. Besides, if they were to have breakfast together at nine, that gave her only three hours to pull herself together.

Still, Lory accomplished nothing until she heard Mike's door close. Restless and unable to deny the reason for that restlessness, she turned on the TV, but the early-morning cartoons and religious programs didn't achieve what she needed them to. Thinking about Mike standing naked in his shower had sent an unaccustomed urgency cascading over her. Knowing he was no longer in the next room was the first step toward sanity, but it would take a great deal more than his absence to restore the equilibrium Lory had always taken for granted. Forcing her thoughts to the mundane, Lory took a thorough inventory of her clothing before selecting jeans and another of her sleeveless T-shirts to take into the bathroom with her.

This was ridiculous. How could she expect Mike to equal what she was feeling if nothing she owned reflected the woman coming to life? Once she must have had a varied wardrobe. What had happened to the dresses she occasionally wore while representing the forest service, the slacks and sweaters she'd lived in while in college, the—Lory's memory deserted her. She couldn't remember buying anything except jeans in the past two years.

That had to be remedied. The thought was a safe one, one maybe capable of extinguishing the flame. Since the forest service supplied much of what she wore on the fire line, she certainly had the money to update her wardrobe. And she needed the activity, any activity. That was what she'd do, soon. She'd go shopping.

Making that decision and fantasizing about what she'd buy consumed the first five minutes Lory was in the tub, but although she was once again in control of her emotions, the prospect of shopping wasn't enough to keep her mind off Mike and what had taken place between them last night.

The situation was too complicated. Why should the sounds of a man going through his morning ritual capture her so completely when she'd spent her life around men? They had a lot in common; they were obviously attracted to each other. Why couldn't she have simply said yes last night? Certainly she would have been more at peace with her body this morning. Thousands, maybe millions of other women wouldn't have driven themselves half crazy with questions and indecision. They wouldn't have blinked over the opportunity to spend the night with an exciting, fascinating, to say nothing of incredibly sexy man.

Lory finished soaking and stood up as the tub emptied. Through the steam she could make out her reflection in the mirror. Her eyes said it all—there was so much more to her than a woman in a man's arms. "You know why you didn't sleep with him," she said aloud. "One night. That's all you'd have. One night."

If only she had some guidelines. If only she'd been this way before.

Silence flooded the room. The walls had no answers. She had to do this alone. And this morning the only thing Lory knew to do was to stop needing more from Mike than a single magic night of lovemaking.

Although she did her best to erase what she did for a living from her body, Lory wasn't particularly pleased with the results. She'd taken care with her makeup and even broken out her hair curler, but the feminine features and softly waving hair made a strange contrast with her no-nonsense outfit. It was going to be a hot summer day; the least she could do was wear sandals instead of tennis shoes, if she had sandals.

What did she care about clothes or shoes? Shopping wasn't what she wanted to do, maybe ever. The past was breaking free. Lory could speak Jeff's name without tears. It was the present, and the future that frightened her. That was why she continued to stare at her faded tennis shoes.

Giving up, Lory grabbed her motel key and stepped outside. The motel complex had been built in a newly developed area of the city. Although there was an abundance of restaurants and gas stations, Lory was unable to find anything within walking distance that resembled a clothing store. Besides, it was too early for anything to be open. Finding a bathing suit would have to wait.

But she couldn't return to the room which was too much at odds with the way she lived her life, and stare at cartoons. What she was feeling needed to be expressed in activity.

At a nearby coffee shop Lory met a retired couple who were traveling in their mobile home. Although they were disappointed that Lory didn't live in Idaho Falls and thus be able to supply them with some information about the city, they invited her to join them for a cup of coffee. Happily Lory accepted the invitation. By the time they'd finished, Lory had seen pictures of five grandchildren, the two dogs back in the mobile home, even the trailer they'd had before buying the mobile home.

Lory waved them off, glanced back at the overhead clock for affirmation that she'd killed over an hour in the coffee shop and headed back toward the motel. Talking to the couple had allowed her to put emotional space between herself and Mike. She barely knew him. Their surroundings had thrown things out of perspective, that's all. They would spend the day together in simple pleasures. And when the day was over she wouldn't ask for more.

When she found him already in the suite, waiting for her, Lory was able to give him a jaunty salute. She even managed to keep her eyes on his face. The only thing she didn't dare do was get close. He, too, seemed to be keeping distance between them. "I've been playing tourist," she explained. "I met the sweetest couple." Lory stopped. Mike's features remained impassive. He didn't care who she'd been with. "Were you able to find whatever part it was you were looking for?" she asked.

"The rotor clutch. I'll tell you over breakfast," Mike said without taking a step toward her. "Have you caught the smells coming from the motel restaurant?"

Lory had. By now her empty stomach was reacting negatively to too much black coffee. It was time to eat. Still holding on to her positive mood with iron fingers, Lory linked her arm through Mike's and pulled him out of the suite before their isolation from the world could become an emotional and physical burden. He smelled of after-shave and morning air. They were dangerous aromas better left behind.

She was rattling on a little, telling him about the retired couple, when they were shown to their seats. The morning sun slid in through the large window next to their table, bathing Mike's features in light, taking away the shadows that had been there when they had been in the suite. "I hope I can be like that when I retire," she told Mike. "I mean, they have enough money to do the things they never had time for before. And they have their health."

Mike had been quiet, but now he entered the conversation. Lory sent him a silent, grateful thank-you for the help he was giving her. Although his mother maintained that she was looking forward to traveling to China with a group of teachers next summer, Mike was bothered that she couldn't just pick up and take off. "That's one of the down things about not being married," he said, his wistful tone pulling Lory closer to the mother/son relationship than she wanted to go. "I wish she had someone to be with. I'm not there enough anymore."

"Good heavens, Mike. Your mother expected that. She knew you had to grow up, make your own life."

"I know that. But, Lory, we were so close. It had to leave a void in her life."

"She doesn't sound lonely."

"She isn't. It's me. I'm the one who does the worrying." For the first time today Lory saw Mike smile. What that simple gesture did to her insides forced her to ask a dangerous question. What would have happened to her resolve if he'd given her that smile in the motel room? She was barely able to concentrate while he explained that his mother had, more than once, told him to quit worrying about her. "Every time I bring up her single state, she throws it back at me. She asks me why I haven't gotten married. She wants grandchildren. That woman." Mike smiled his mesmerizing smile again. "She nags me to stay on the ground long enough for a woman to catch me."

"It sounds as if the two of you have an open, honest relationship," Lory observed. She dropped her hands into her lap to stop herself from reaching for Mike. He needed a haircut. There was entirely too much hair, and she ached to hold the healthy strands between her fingers.

"Too honest if you ask me."

"Why *don't* you stay on the ground long enough for a woman to catch you?"

"Do you want the truth, or what I tell my mother?" Mike picked up his fork and poked neat holes through his napkin. "I tell her that it takes time to build up a macho image. It wouldn't do for me to be hanging around the bars looking for action, would it?"

"I never thought about it that way." Lory leaned back as the waitress set eggs, hash browns and bacon in front of her. Her stomach rumbled in anticipation, but her mind wasn't on food. Mike didn't want to talk truth. She had no choice but to go along with the subterfuge. "This macho image business, it really is a burden, isn't it?"

"It can be." Mike was digging into his breakfast. "It's strange the way some women act. The ones who are the first to talk about women's lib and how they're not going to be dependent on any man are the first to tell me how wonderful it is that I'm a self-made success."

"What's wrong with that?"

"Nothing. Except that they're usually giving me that look when they say it."

"What look?"

"I don't know. Like a dog waiting for mealtime."

Lory threw back her head and laughed. With that sound, the tangled emotions she'd brought into the café vanished. It was a beautiful summer morning. "Remind me to never give you that look. You don't need a wife. Just get yourself a basset hound."

For a few minutes Mike concentrated on his meal. When he paused, his eyes settled on Lory, and she wondered if he was discovering her presence in his life all over again. "Why haven't you gotten married?" he asked.

Despite the shock of the unexpected question, Lory felt no desire to sidestep it. "I never felt the need."

"But you've been asked?"

Had she? Once, in high school, she'd almost given in to the romance that was running rampant through the campus. There had been a couple of close calls in college, but nothing had come of them. Since then there'd been work and feeling good about herself. She'd spoken the truth when she'd told Mike she'd never felt the need to share her life with a man. "It depends on how you define being asked," she tried to answer. "A seventeen-year-old football player proposed during the spring prom, but he was sidetracked by a girl on the flag team before I could make up my mind."

"That couldn't have been the only time, Lory. You're an attractive, intelligent woman."

Lory appreciated the compliment, but she wasn't sure what that had to do with anything. "You're talking to a woman with four brothers. There weren't many men who could get through that gauntlet. Also, because of those four pests, I knew just about everything there was to know about boys. I wasn't particularly impressed."

It was Mike's turn to laugh. The sun caught his hair, turning brown into summer red. "I never thought about that. Too many dirty clothes to stumble over. Too many whiskers in the sink. Tell me, is there anything about the male sex that impresses you?"

If that was intended as a loaded question, Lory chose to ignore it. "None that I can think of. The problem with most men is that they're all action and not enough introspection. Don't forget, I've done a great deal of study about this subject. When my brothers and their friends got together, they were always doing things. Always competing with each other. I don't think they ever simply sat down and talked the way the girls did."

Mike continued to smile while Lory was talking, but the glint was gone from his eyes. "Are you saying men don't have good verbal skills? Or is it that they don't feel things that need to be talked about, that they lack depth?"

The conversation had gone from lighthearted to serious, but that didn't bother Lory. "No. I don't think it's that they don't feel things the same way women do. But maybe—" Concentrating, Lory bit her lip. "Maybe it's the way they're raised. I know some of this happened in my family. We expect boys to be physical. To learn how to work on their cars and make the football team. Boys are supposed to be practical and competent. We don't expect them to be sensitive."

"And you think that's a mistake?"

Lory didn't want to give Mike a quick or easy answer. "Yes, I guess I do. Look, I love my brothers. They're terrific men. Just the same, I wouldn't want to be in the position they're in. My parents did what they thought was right, and they certainly raised sons who can go out and compete with anyone. But when they're hit with something in their lives that can't be handled with physical activity, they're at a disadvantage. Curt, he's my oldest brother, his first child was born premature. The baby only lived a few hours. Curt was lost. The only thing he knew to do was ram his fist through a wall. Women can cry. Men haven't been allowed to do that."

"And you want to see men cry?"

"I think they'd be better off if they could." Jeff had been in pain; there had been no safe release for him. "They wouldn't bottle things up inside them. They'd have a safe release. It was a long time before Curt could talk about the baby, a lot longer than it took his wife. I know they hurt the same. It's just that Curt didn't know what to do with the pain."

"That bothers you, doesn't it?" Mike was asking softly. He hadn't picked up his fork since the conversation had taken this turn. "Did any of your other brothers go through this?"

"Not them so much. Life has been good to my family. There was—someone else. I saw pain tear him apart." Kill him.

They finished their meal in silence, but not because that was the way Mike wanted it. The brick wall Mike had found himself being slammed up against last night had resurfaced. Lory had said she'd never had a serious proposal, or at least she hadn't taken it seriously, but there was someone—something he couldn't get a handle on. He could see it in her eyes and hear it in her tone. He wanted to know what was going through her now. But how could he if she wasn't going to offer? They were too new with each other. There wasn't enough of a base.

"Are you ready for that swim?" Mike asked after paying for the meal. "I'm not sure it's such a good idea on a full stomach."

Lory linked her arm through Mike's. Mike had been too quiet. She thought she knew why. They'd been too serious, so it was time for a lighter tone. "What I'd like is to go shopping."

"For what?"

Lory laughed at the wary note she was hearing. An indisputable sign that one of her brothers was in love was allowing himself to be dragged into a shopping expedition with the woman. No wonder Mike sounded dismayed. He wasn't in love. "A bathing suit," Lory explained.

"I was going to get you one. But I couldn't find any stores open."

"You were going to what?"

"Buy you a bathing suit."

"Mike." Lory stopped him. "I can't let you do that."

"Why not?" He looked confused. "You don't have one. That outfit you have, well—I want us to go swimming in public."

"Mike," she repeated. "That's personal. I can't let you buy my clothes."

"I paid for the motel room."

Lory refused to allow the debate to go further. True, she'd already accepted a great deal from him. But a bathing suit? No. She couldn't allow that.

Despite the promise she'd made to grab the first thing that looked presentable, Lory wound up having Mike take her to three stores before she found something that wouldn't embarrass her in public. Although the sides of the one-piece black tank suit she finally settled on were cut higher than she would have liked, at least she wouldn't have to show off her untanned middle. The suit also had the built-in support her full breasts needed.

"Now I do need to go swimming," Lory gasped as they left the department store. "That's tiring."

"You don't want to do any more shopping? I thought you were just getting a full head of steam up."

"Are you kidding? My wardrobe looks like Mother Hubbard's cupboard, but there's only so much punishment I can take in one day." Forget what I said earlier about shopping, Lory told herself. Maybe next year.

When they returned to the motel, Lory disappeared into her half of the suite. She hauled on her suit and was waiting, towel tucked under her arm, by the time Mike joined

her. Once again he was wearing nothing except that inadequate piece of black fabric. "I have to warn you," she
managed. "I'm a good swimmer. And eager." Lory took a
halting step in the direction of the front door.

Although Mike had seen her take the suit into the dressing room, he hadn't seen it on her. Now he wouldn't be distracted by her impatience. All morning she'd been skating
just out of his reach. Reason said that what she'd been doing
was wise; emotion said he'd had enough of reason. "In a
minute, Lory. We have time—for a lot of things." He
pushed her away from the door. "Turn around. I want to
know if it was worth a couple of hours out of my life."

"We weren't shopping for a couple of hours," Lory tried
to protest. The look on Mike's face stopped her. *He ap-
proves.*

"It looks good on you. A lot better than those things with
flowers and bows and who knows what else. I still wish
you'd let me buy it for you."

"Thank you for saying that." Lory supposed she should
be protesting again that she didn't accept gifts from men,
but Mike wasn't trying to buy her favors with money—he'd
already proven that. And she wasn't going to cheapen
whatever it was they had by bringing the issue up again.
"That's sweet."

"It's right for you."

Flustered, Lory grabbed at the fabric that left too much
of her hip revealed. "I guess they're all made this way these
days. It feels strange."

"You have the legs for it."

The conversation was getting out of control. "Are...you
ready?"

"In a minute." Lory knew. Mike was going to take her
arms and draw her against him. Too much flesh would
touch. Too many words left unsaid would hang in the air.
"First—I haven't kissed you today."

Lory had been aware of that. Acutely aware. She hadn't known whether she was relieved or sorry that she hadn't allowed the opportunity to present itself before, but with his lips inches from hers, she knew she couldn't back away. She'd fought this moment all morning. It had been a good fight, but the time for surrender had come.

When their lips met, Lory wasn't sure which one of them had done the most to make it happen. His hands slid from her arms to her bare back, covering her flesh with warmth and promise.

A kiss, make it only a kiss. Her body didn't hear the words, though. She was reaching for the support his neck offered; her right leg was seeking and making contact with his left. It wasn't that different from the way their legs had touched in the tub the previous night, except that this time there was no hot water blunting the effect. With the contact, Lory lost her separate identity.

She clung to him, acknowledging the impact he was having on her senses and her helplessness in the face of that impact. What was it she'd said she wanted to do? There must have been something, but the thought was lost, stripped away. Replaced by something primitive and essential.

Today Lory was the first to open her mouth and escalate their kiss to another level. She was moving restlessly against Mike, seeking gratification that would never come as long as black fabric stood between them. In the space of a heartbeat, modesty no longer mattered. She needed to taste, to explore, to probe, to absorb the full impact of his assault on her. Mike's hands were resting on the swell of her hips, pulling her against him. Last night she'd resisted. Today she felt no need to end the contact.

This was what she'd been born for, why, without thinking, she'd jumped on what might be a speeding train without brakes. Bold, thinking nothing of the danger, Lory moved with him, pressing her body against his as if pressure alone could slash away the cloth barriers.

When he moaned in response, Lory slid her hands from Mike's neck until she'd found his chest. She opened her eyes, smiling when she read the impact her touch was having on him. This man could be hers; she held him in the palm of her hand. Her power both frightened and thrilled her.

Who had the power? It wasn't Lory who was in control. Mike's touch turned her into putty. His kiss left her on the verge of tears, needing more. Reeling in helplessness, Lory twisted until she could touch every possible inch of his flesh. They wouldn't make love. No. They weren't ready for that. But—

"Do you have any idea what you're doing to me?" Mike whispered against her ear. Lory trembled when his breath touched her sensitive flesh. For a moment the question made no sense.

"I think so," she managed through the rising tide. "I know what's happening to me."

"Is it wise?"

"What?" Lory reached for Mike's mouth again, but he wouldn't let her.

"Last night you didn't want this to happen." His fingers now gripping her arms were leaving white indentations.

"Mike? It isn't wrong."

"Maybe not this." Boldly Mike cupped his hands around her waiting breasts. "But can we stop at this?"

He was right. So damn right she wanted to hate him for saying it. They'd had a few more hours together, but those hours still weren't enough for intimacy. Taking the second step without taking time for the first was a fool's mission.

But the tide was still rising in her; the second step was a breath away. If she didn't turn from it now, she might reveal everything, let Mike know that the power was his.

"Are you ready to go?"

Mike wasn't, but he acquiesced to what he perceived as Lory's greater wisdom. Asking her whether she was ready for them to become lovers had been a last faltering stab at sanity. A moment more with her in his arms and he wouldn't have been able to utter a word. Now he didn't know whether he was relieved or angry with her answer.

"Anytime you are." He opened the door, walked out and then remembered to wait for her. Walking toward the inner court with its free-form-shaped swimming pool was the last thing he wanted to be doing, and yet because he was caught in the fluid magic of her steps, Mike was able to keep his legs in motion.

Pretending a casualness that wasn't there, Mike took Lory's hand, swinging their arms in unison until they were in the huge high-ceilinged room that contained potted plants, a separate wading pool and a sitting area in addition to the pool.

Taking a deep breath to control the slowly subsiding tide, Lory spoke. "I think we're going to have to fight for the slide." Lory pointed with her free hand at the long slide jutting over the water. Three boys were squabbling over whose turn it was to go down.

The water, although not as hypnotically warm as that in the hot tub, went a long way toward returning Lory to sanity. A few minutes after entering the water, she forced herself to concentrate on swimming laps. Once she'd expended some of her seemingly endless energy, she challenged Mike to a race, but the pool was too crowded for any power strokes. Besides, swimming too close to Mike might stir the tide again.

Without telling him why she was doing it, Lory swam away from him. Watching children, nodding at adults, trying to ignore the glances of those sitting around the edge, took Lory both physically and mentally away from the man in the skin-hugging black suit. Now when she saw that he'd been cornered by a couple of teenage girls, she could give him a casual salute before taking her place in line for the slide. It had been a dream, those few moments back in their motel room. A beautiful, sensual, unreal dream. Lory Foster wasn't the kind of woman to trade sanity for a few moments of pleasure.

They swam and played for the better part of an hour. Then they climbed out of the pool and found a couple of lounge chairs to stretch out on. The sun coming in through the domed glass roof was warm and comforting. Lory drifted off. She wasn't awake when Mike left her. He slipped a shirt over his shoulders and walked barefoot to the motel office. Ignoring the disapproving glare of the desk clerk, he asked to use the telephone.

"I don't care where it is," he told the voice on the other end of the line. "It'll take me a couple of hours to replace a part on the chopper, but I can be there before dark. Yeah. You could say I need the money."

The first lie didn't bother him, but the one he had to tell after he'd shaken Lory awake very nearly undid his resolve. "Lory? I have to go to work," he told her.

"What? How did they find you here?"

"I left the motel number with the Interagency Fire Center."

"Why?"

"Why?" Mike repeated. This wasn't coming out right. He should have the guts to tell her the truth. "I have a sense of responsibility, Lory. When I think I'm needed, I go."

Lory didn't try to argue down his sense of responsibility. Neither, he understood, did she buy what he had told her. But she didn't know. Couldn't understand. In the short time Mike had known Lory Foster, the woman had done things to him emotionally that had never been done to him before, asked far more of him than he'd given before.

Mike Steen didn't know what to do with the request. He needed back his space.

HAD THEIR TIME TOGETHER really happened? Or had it all been a fantasy born of her need to have a man—that man—in her life? For the next week that question was never more than a heartbeat away. Even when she was once again caught up in the treadmill of her life, when she least wanted it, Lory's mind slipped back to their time in the hot tub, her thoughts when she'd heard Mike moving about in his room, the breakfast they'd shared, the moments of near abandon before they'd fled for the swimming pool.

What hurt was the way Mike had left her. What made her angry was his refusal to be honest. Before she had fully understood what was happening, they'd checked out of the motel and driven back to the airport. Silent, Lory had watched Mike make the necessary repairs. Although he'd offered to take her to wherever the hotshot team would be reassembled, Lory knew it wasn't what he wanted to do. He'd put emotional space between them. He didn't want or need her anymore. All right—she wouldn't beg.

Hurting, angry, proud, Lory had assured him that Keith wouldn't be looking for her for another day. Then, after she'd told him that she intended to stay in Idaho Falls one more night before calling the foreman, she'd had to stand alone while the Sikorsky had lifted Mike Steen slowly into the sky.

Igor had taken Mike from her. The soft, wordless kiss just before he'd settled behind the controls hadn't been enough. He hadn't said anything about seeing her again, and with her pride wrapped tightly around her, Lory hadn't said anything, either.

It was better that way, she'd told herself when she had no longer been able to make out Mike's profile. Until the hot, dry summer was behind them, neither of them had enough control over their lives.

But why not a single word? Why the sudden distance slammed between them like bars wielded by an angry jailer? They'd been close for a while. Lory knew that. But Mike no longer wanted that. Lory was left with nothing except the gentle, faltering kiss that wouldn't leave her heart.

"I'm just not ready for anything," she tried to tell Ann when the other fire fighter grilled her about her vacation. "Ann, you know how I was after Jeff. It's safer if I don't get too close to anyone right now."

"Bull!" Ann snorted. "It's not the same thing and you know it. That's one sexy, exciting man. And you're not the type for a one-night stand. I won't buy that that's all you wanted out of it."

Lory didn't try to correct Ann's impression of what had happened. The only thing she did was lie to herself. Mike was married to his helicopter. Like a fall leaf caught by the wind, he drifted where the wind blew him. He'd entered her life for a few precious hours, but fortunately, before he could become too important to her, the wind had sent him spinning in another direction.

"It was fun while it lasted," she told Ann. "I think every woman should do that once in their life."

But nothing had happened. That's what kept Lory awake at nights. What they'd had hadn't been enough.

Chapter Seven

Mike was on what he hoped was the last of three days of duty in eastern Washington when the radio dispatcher informed him that he had a personal message, one the dispatcher didn't think should wait. "No, I don't know what she wants. All I know is, if I got a message from someone who sounded like that, I'd be bowling people over getting to the phone."

Although he was alone when he received the message, Mike nodded. He knew what Lory's voice sounded like in person. If anything, the tones would become deeper, richer with every mile that separated them. "Give me that number again," he told the dispatcher. "And, no, it is not any of your business."

For the rest of the day, Lory's name and voice remained in the cockpit with Mike, but it wasn't until he touched down at an airfield outside Colvile and located a telephone that he was able to put an end to the questions that had haunted him while he should have been tending to business. For close to two weeks he'd been telling himself that distance was what he and Lory needed. What he needed anyway. But with her phone number in front of him, his resolve went out the window. He didn't give himself time to think before punching the numbers.

Lory picked up the receiver on the fourth ring.

"It's Mike," he introduced himself unnecessarily. "I got your message."

"Oh." For too long Lory didn't say anything else. Then she asked, "Where are you?"

"Some private airport somewhere. Making money, unfortunately. A logging operation, which should have been closed down under these dry conditions, got out of hand from what I've heard. Everyone's pointing fingers at someone else. Where are you?"

"Home. But it isn't going to last long. I leave at dawn."

Home? What was it she'd told him, that she had a place overlooking the Snake? That wasn't right. He should know where Lory Foster lived. "Where are you going?"

Lory's laugh put emotion into her disembodied voice. "I forgot to ask. Keith said to pack for a week, but he exaggerates a lot. Mike? The connection is terrible."

"I know." Anger, unexpected yet real, slashed through him. He needed a reminder of what was warm and human about Lory and all he had was her voice. Except for the laugh, she could have been the operator. Had it only been two weeks since he'd talked to her? It felt like a year. "Are you all right?"

"Yes, of course. Why do you ask?"

"The only message I got was that you wanted me to call. What are you doing home? You weren't injured, were you?"

"Of course not." Again Lory's laugh reached him. "You know what Idaho's like this month. Between the rangelands and the Rocky Mountains, it's like everything's waiting in line to catch fire. We've been fighting fires here since—since the last time I saw you. Mike? What are you doing next weekend?"

Mike, whose life was scheduled from day to day in the summer, had no idea. "Beats me. What are you doing next weekend?" he asked when the loud hissing subsided.

"I hope I'm going to be showing you the Snake."

She wants to see me. Despite what I did to her, she wants to see me. It shouldn't mean that much, but it did. There was no way Mike could deny that. "Are you sure you can get the time off?"

"I've already conned Keith into it. Mike, my parents are holding a family reunion. My brothers have juggled their vacations and their kids are out of school, so everyone's going to be there. I was the one they couldn't pin down."

She went on to explain that he could fly to a private landing strip near Rupert Friday night. Lory would pick him up and drive him to where the clan was assembling. They hoped to be under way by nine the next morning.

"It's a little like the landing of the Marines," Lory finished up. "If you don't want to go, just say so."

"I want to go. Lory, why did you ask me?"

"Because . . . I want you there."

That was all Mike needed to hear. Nothing, not even the prospect of being asked to account for his behavior in Idaho Falls, could keep him away.

LORY KNEW SHE WAS TOO EARLY as she parked her parents' pickup with the name Snake Adventures on it next to the lone hangar. Except for a private Cessna, the airstrip outside the town was empty. She shut off the ignition and stepped out to absorb the hot, dry late afternoon. The air smelled of irrigated farmland.

Her hands strayed to her sides, but she stopped herself from wiping her damp palms on the new cream slacks she'd bought only a few hours ago. She stepped carefully to avoid getting pebbles in the leather sandals she'd dug out of the bottom of her closet. Lory didn't know where she was headed, only that standing still was impossible.

Would Mike come? Or had she scared him off with her aggressiveness and the threat of a large family gathering? This uncertainty was unlike Lory, but wanting and asking a man to spend time with her was a new experience. True, she'd occasionally invited other fire fighters to take advantage of her parents' recreational services, but those times she'd been acting in her capacity as a promoter of Snake Adventures. This was the first time the man was more important than increased business.

Before she could stop herself, Lory's hands slid down over the smooth fabric. If this was what men went through when they asked a woman out, she had the utmost sympathy for them. If Mike didn't show up, would she be able to pretend to her family that it didn't matter? Would she try to pretend to herself?

Lory was relieved to find that someone was working on the Cessna, and struck up a conversation. She killed fifteen minutes by pretending that she was interested in flying lessons and asked questions about the cost and maintenance of a private plane. Finally, though, the elderly gentleman's wife arrived to take him home. Lory was left alone.

The wind had kicked up, but Lory couldn't detect any lowering in air temperature, when her ears isolated the sound she had to hear. In the distance a dot was getting larger, taking on definition. Mike had come, after all.

She took refuge behind the hangar as Mike brought the silver Sikorsky down. She didn't wait for the blades to stop revolving before ducking her head and hurrying toward him. At the last moment she pulled up short. The final steps were taken at a slow walk. She didn't dare appear too eager. He might guess too much.

"How was your flight?" she asked when he'd closed the door behind him. The moisture she'd wiped off her hands was back; she certainly couldn't offer her hand for a shake. But a kiss? No. Maybe he didn't want that.

"Routine." Mike had stepped out from under the blades, but now he, too, was standing with his hands hanging at his sides. "Is that your folks' truck?"

Lory nodded, wincing at the insanity of their twin questions. How were they going to spend a weekend together if they couldn't think of anything to say to each other?

Mike looked larger, stronger, than she remembered. He was wearing the jeans and boots that were a part of him, but his golf shirt looked as new as the white summer-weight blouse she was wearing. Knowing that he'd put on a new shirt for her gave her courage. Somehow she found words to fill the silence while he unloaded and then threw his belongings into the back of the pickup.

Lory slid behind the wheel and concentrated on starting the truck. He hadn't kissed her. Hadn't said anything about being glad to see her. Thank heavens she hadn't made a fool of herself by reaching for him. "Just about everyone's there already," she chattered in an attempt to cover the pain caused by the distance separating them. "My kid brother and his latest should be there by dinner. The grandkids are driving Grandpa nuts trying to help."

"How many grandchildren are there?"

Lory made a great show of counting up five grandsons and three granddaughters, but her mind wasn't on her nieces and nephews. How would Mike react to it all? She couldn't blame him if he turned tail and ran. The whole thing had been a mistake. She should never have called him.

But he was so close. She could feel his body heat in the hot interior, feel his life force. Lory tried to ask him for specifics of what he'd been doing for the past two weeks, but it was almost impossible. He'd had time to get in touch with her. And hadn't. Why did he have to be the only one who handled their being together without feeling as if he were about to fly apart?

Damn her, Mike thought. With her white blouse and im-
maculate slacks, she was everything he wasn't. From the
first day Mike had been impressed by Lory's cool head and
easy competence, but this evening he'd do anything to find
a chink in the armor. What a fool he'd been to spend the
flight here worrying that she'd ask about his abrupt departure in Idaho Falls. Obviously it didn't mean that much to
her. She was calmly telling him about what they'd encoun-
ter at her parents' place while he practically had to sit on his
hands to keep from touching her.

What he was was a damn fool and a liar. Two weeks
hadn't blunted what he felt.

Mike didn't know what he expected Snake Adventures to
look like, so the ranchlike setting with rafts, riverboats and
equipment everywhere placed within sight of the broad,
slowly moving river didn't faze him. He even took in stride
the collection of vehicles and children running about.

"Mike?" Lory asked as she pulled into a parking slot.
"There's going to be questions about us. And some teasing."

"I kind of figured there might be. Don't worry." He gave
her a smile. "I can handle it."

Mike was ready to amend that slightly when, an hour
later, the clan was gathering for dinner. In that hour he'd
been introduced to three wives, four brothers and a young
lady who looked almost as intimidated as he felt and clung
close to Lory's youngest brother. The kids, except for a ten-
month-old who pegged his legs as exactly what he needed to
hold himself erect, were pretty much a blur.

He had to hand it to Lory's mother. With a minimum of
help from her daughters-in-law, she managed to come up
with enough fried chicken, mashed potatoes and fresh string
beans to feed the crowd eating on the deck overlooking the
river. Mike had been concerned that the Foster clan might
believe in more formality than he was used to, but practi-

cality was the order of the day. Still, he wasn't quite sure how he'd wound up holding the baby on his lap while his mother fed him mashed potatoes.

It was a rather messy procedure, which made Mike glad that jeans could repel mashed potatoes. At first the wiggling bundle in his arms made him uneasy, not because he didn't want to hold the baby, but because he wasn't sure he was doing things right. But once he realized that as long as he kept his hand wrapped around the baby's waist, Bouncer wasn't going to escape, Mike relaxed.

This part of the reunion was pure unadulterated pleasure, as was having Lory sitting next to him. Listening to her talk to one of her sisters-in-law gave Mike the opportunity to observe her ability to find a common ground with someone who understood almost nothing of Lory's world. From what he gathered, Margo Foster had worked as a secretary in an investment firm until deciding to go back to school a couple of years ago. Now she had completed her business courses and was knocking on doors looking for a job that would make the most of her new skills. Mike found her discussion of firms that refused to see her as anything more than a secretary interesting but removed from his world. Lory, however, seemed genuinely interested in everything Margo had to say. Lory did more than listen. She suggested several ways Margo could play up her recent education that Margo hadn't thought of.

Mike lost his grip on what he was doing; he was being absorbed by Lory's presence, voice, thoughts. If he'd found it difficult to keep his hands off her in the truck, only the baby on his lap now kept him from wrapping her in his arms.

He'd been such a damn fool. Being alone wasn't what he'd needed at all. She was the wise one, the one with the guts to pick up the phone and give them another chance.

A chuckle from the baby's mother stopped Mike's thoughts. He turned to see that Bouncer had picked a piece of potato off his jeans and was trying to feed it to him. Mike grinned and opened his mouth to receive the cold blob. He made loud smacking sounds, which encouraged the baby to try again. The second blob contained just enough lint to make swallowing difficult. When he was offered a third morsel, Mike shook his head and tried to aim the baby's pudgy fingers in a safe direction.

"You're going to have to divert him," Lory offered. "Give him something to eat."

Warming to the challenge, Mike took a chunk of home-made roll off his plate and handed it to Bouncer. The potato glob plopped back onto his jeans as the youngster took the new offering. "I'm a fast learner," Mike observed. With his free hand, he plucked the lump off his leg.

"Not fast enough," Lory chuckled. "I take it you haven't had much experience around a baby with a mouthful to gum."

A minute later Mike understood what Lory was getting at. If he thought the baby's table manners left something to be desired before, it was nothing compared to the sticky mess the roll had become. Mike gave the mother a desperate look, but she'd been distracted by something one of her older children was asking her. When Mike turned his eyes on Lory, she laughed out loud. "Don't look at me, fella. You got yourself into this mess, you get yourself out of it." A moment later she'd apparently taken pity on him, because she first wiped the baby's chin and then took the youngster from him.

A strange combination of relief and emptiness washed over Mike. Relief because he didn't feel secure in his role as surrogate parent; emptiness because he'd experienced a child's friendship and had had that taken from him.

After dinner Lory's brothers took off with their father to make last-minute preparations for the trip while the women started clearing the eating area. For one of the few times in his life Mike felt useless. Jamming his hands into his back pockets, he walked to the railing and stared out at the deeply rumbling river. The setting sun had changed the Snake from blue to rose. It might have been a trick of the eye, but he thought he saw a fish surface. With the children now in the house, Mike was aware of the deep silence. Lory had told him that her place was about ten miles to the east and even closer to the river. Someday, somehow, he'd learn what impact the river had had in forming her.

"It really is magnificent, isn't it?"

Mike turned to find that Lory's mother had joined him. "Yes, it is." He'd had little opportunity to get to know Lory's parents, but he'd been struck by their vitality. Janet Foster was shorter than her daughter and carried no more extra flesh. Her hair had been allowed to gray naturally. Her skin wore the imprint of close to sixty years spent out-of-doors. "You have a beautiful place," he said softly.

"It suits us. It isn't particularly modern, and the TV reception stinks, but it would take an earthquake to move me. Lory says you fly a helicopter."

Because he wanted someone to talk to, Mike described what he did for a living. He didn't say anything about how he and Lory had met, guessing that the two women had already discussed this. "My mother would like this place."

"Maybe she can come here sometime."

How easily this woman extended her invitation. Mike wondered if Janet Foster was trying to further her daughter's relationship with him, but that didn't fit in with what he knew of the woman. If Lory's mother had been domineering, she wouldn't have wanted Lory to become a fire fighter. "Maybe she can," Mike responded. "I keep telling her she isn't getting any younger. She needs to explore more of the country.''

Janet laughed. ''Didn't your mother tell you that it isn't nice to bring up her age?''

''Yeah. But I can outrun her, so she can't stop me.''

Again Janet laughed. The chuckle was so like Lory's that it caught him unawares. Mike loved Lory's laugh. ''Actually,'' Mike made himself go on, ''she is going to start doing some exploring pretty soon. She needs to teach two more years before she can retire, but after that I don't think anything is going to hold her back.''

''That sounds like me.'' Janet had joined Mike at the railing. She leaned forward, eyes intent on the constant flow a few hundred feet away. ''I've put in my years in a kitchen. Why do you think I have three and a half daughters-in-law? Let them do the cleaning up. I'm going to do what I darn well please.''

''Which is what?''

''Which is get to know you. Lory hasn't told me much, but that's the way that girl is.'' Janet winked at Mike. ''It was so hard for her to get a word in edgewise while she was growing up. I wish she'd talk more, but we can't change a person's nature. Not even our children's. Anyway.'' Janet winked again. ''Tell me all about yourself.''

''There isn't much to tell.''

''Everyone has a story, Mike. How did you wind up in a helicopter?''

For the next fifteen minutes Mike told his story to an appreciative audience. He hadn't told many people about his frustration with the way large corporations operated, and his need to get out from under the structured environment, but with Janet nodding in agreement, he found the explaining easy. Janet countered with comments about some of the problems Snake Adventures had complying with governmental rules and regulations. By the time the other women joined them, Mike was convinced that Lory's intellect could be traced to her mother. He was also convinced that he and Janet Foster could meet twenty years in the future and find something to talk about.

Lory came out with her youngest brother's girlfriend. The two women were deep in conversation about her and Curt's problems with their landlord, but the moment Lory spotted Mike, she lost her train of thought. While in the kitchen, she'd been torn between doing her share of the chores and wanting to rescue Mike. She'd hoped he'd been asked to join the men, but neither her father nor her brothers were used to making concessions for someone who didn't know how to do what they took for granted.

Lory opened her mouth to apologize for deserting him, but closed it when she saw the easy way he and her mother were standing together watching the endless flow, listening to the age-old sound. *He belongs here. He could become part of us.*

"We wondered where you disappeared to," Lory teased her mother as she joined them. Her voice wasn't strong enough. "Always ducking out when there's work to be done in the kitchen."

"I fixed the meal," her mother shot back. "You girls can darn well clean up my mess. Besides—" she stared up at Mike "—he's a lot more interesting than you."

"Thanks a lot, Mom." It was almost dark now. Lory could hear but not see the river. The sound was as much a part of her as the sound of her own voice, a comforting rumble that took away some of the tension she felt. There were so many things she wanted to say to Mike, but not with others around.

"I've heard everything you have to say," Janet was saying. "I know your life story. I didn't know Mike's."

"I can't believe you know his whole life story already," Lory pointed out. She felt Mike's eyes on her, sensed that he was tuned to everything she might say. "How's the packing coming? Do you think we'll really get off first thing in the morning?"

"You know your father," Janet observed. "That man's so punctual he drives me crazy."

Janet launched into a lengthy tale about the difficulties of living with a man who believed that being late was a sin. Lory wanted to drag Mike away so that he wouldn't have to listen, but she didn't know how to do it without insulting her mother. Janet didn't usually say much about the private nature of her marriage. Maybe it was being surrounded by her daughters-in-law that was responsible for her reflective mood.

Lory hoped Mike would understand. Her parents had a solid marriage, but like any two people who'd been married for more than thirty years, there were bound to be little irritations.

But maybe he didn't understand. He hadn't seen a marriage in action. He had no experience with the kind of give and take and tolerance and love it took to survive those years.

The return of the men coupled with the increasing irritability of tired children put an end to the conversation. As the women wandered off, Lory remained on the deck hoping Mike would stay with her. He did. "I don't know if they're going to be able to get the kids to sleep," she observed when at last they were alone. "They're pretty excited."

"I don't blame them." Mike had turned away from the river and was facing her in the dark. His voice lowered and became part of the sounds of nature. "I know I'm looking forward to it."

Lory shivered. His voice had the power to do so much to her. "You are? I thought, well, I'm glad we haven't scared you off."

"I don't scare that easy, Lory."

Why did the way he spoke her name have that effect? It was going to be next to impossible to keep the conversation going. "I didn't mean it that way," she amended. "It's just that it's quite a crowd. You're used to things being quieter."

"It doesn't hurt me to experience something new. Your mother's quite a woman. Raising five children and helping to run a business. I admire her."

"Yes, she is quite a woman." Lory couldn't think of anything else to say. She stood, stiff and awkward, wanting something to happen, afraid that something might. She wanted to be relaxed around Mike, to link her hand with his without worrying about his reaction. She wanted to believe the thoughts that had struck her when she found him on the deck. But he'd given her a message the last time they'd been together. There was distance between them. Until he was ready to lower the barriers, she had no choice but to live by his rules. And if those barriers were never removed...

"Have you always lived here?" Mike asked.

"What?" At least they could talk. Taking comfort in that, Lory supplied him with an answer. "Since I was a toddler. The place wasn't much when we first moved in and there wasn't the money to do anything with it for several years. But then the business got off the ground and we kids were old enough to help."

"With the business?"

"And with expanding the house." Lory pointed to the left side of the house. "We added three bedrooms and something I guess you'd call a den. We also had to reroof what was already there, put in new plumbing, you name it."

"And you helped?"

"Of course I helped. Why wouldn't I?"

"No reason." Mike was silent for several minutes. "There isn't much you won't tackle, is there?"

"I guess not." Lory wasn't sure where the conversation was heading. Grabbing a hammer and nail apron and joining her brothers on the roof had been as natural as joining them on the school bus.

"I like that."

Of all the things Mike could have said, that was the best. "Why?"

"Why?" Mike threw her question back at her. "I guess, because that's the way I think it should be. Lory? I don't know if I said it, but thank you for asking me here."

She'd been skirting around the issue; they'd both been skirting around it. Now she felt as if she'd plunged into a deep river. It would be a moment before she knew whether she could swim. "I wasn't sure whether I should."

"Because of the way I acted the last time?"

Lory nodded. "I didn't understand."

Mike held out his hands and waited until she'd placed hers in them. "I'm not sure I did, either." Warmth flowed from his fingers to hers, making the night right, making her world right. "I'd like to talk to you about that, but I'm not sure how the words will come out."

Maybe she couldn't fight the tide caused by his words, by his touch, but Lory had at least reached the surface. "We'll talk when you're ready." Although he hadn't tried to draw her closer, Lory took her clue from his gentle touch. She slid forward until her body registered his presence. After that Mike took over. He drew her against him and cupped a hand around her jaw. Lory had closed her eyes before the contact was made.

She'd waited so long to feel Mike's lips. It had been a lifetime of wanting and hurting and wondering, but those agonies no longer existed. She was in his arms. They were together again.

Mike hadn't known he was going to kiss Lory until his mouth was absorbing her soft warmth. His heart was trying to beat in time with hers. *Take it easy,* he'd told himself while they were talking. *One step at a time. You don't know what you're feeling.*

But Mike did know what he was feeling, at least part of what he was feeling. Those emotions had very little to do with respecting her intellect and a great deal to do with wanting to lead her into the dark, sharing her with no one. Knowing she was sleeping in the next room at the motel had required a great deal of self-control, but that was nothing compared to the struggle he was going through now.

It was incredible. Absolutely incredible! Two weeks of absence hadn't blunted his feelings at all.

Mike tried to satisfy himself with the explanation that what he felt was purely physical, but as he felt Lory's growing response, he knew it was much more complicated than that. Yes, he had all he could do to keep from slipping her out of her clothes where they stood. But if he was honest with himself, he had to admit that fantasy wouldn't become reality unless Lory wanted the same thing. She was more, much more, than a very feminine body. She was also the mind he'd come to admire, the emotions he was just starting to explore.

This wasn't something he'd felt before. Desire Mike Steen could cope with. Having his heart insist on entering the picture was more than he was ready to deal with tonight.

"The walls have ears," he whispered, pushing Lory away so that he was no longer mesmerized by her lips.

"It won't surprise them." *Kiss him again. Continue what just began.* But Lory fought off the impulse. Once before she'd come close to Mike only to have him draw back. She sensed the same thing happening again. "About the sleeping arrangements."

"What about the sleeping arrangements?"

"This is my parents' house. I know they want me to live my own life, but—"

"I understand," Mike said, making it easier for her. "Where do you want me to sleep?"

"I'm afraid it'll have to be on the floor. In a room with my nephews."

To Lory's relief, Mike laughed. "It sounds like a slumber party. Don't let it bother you, Lory." He turned somber. "I won't lie. I wish we were together." Now even his eyes no longer carried the image of laughter. "We need that, Lory."

Mike turned from her, his eyes once again seeking the source of the constant, faint rumble. For another minute Lory stood where he'd left her, but his back was too much for her to handle. She'd all but stripped herself naked by asking him here. Was this all he was going to give her? She half lifted her hands as if to touch him, but quit before the contact could be made. Wordless, she turned away and walked into the house.

Chapter Eight

Wise in the dual impact of bright sunshine and water on skin, Lory was careful to cover her arms and legs with suntan lotion before leaving the next morning. Because the morning air was chilled, she pulled a sweatshirt over her bathing suit. Mike, too, was adequately prepared. He'd exchanged his boots for old tennis shoes that would grip and was wearing a sweatshirt over his trunks and a baseball cap on his head.

As the two met at their raft with their belongings, Mike tipped his cap gallantly. "Top of the morning, ma'am. You're looking particularly ravishing today."

Lory stuck out a long, slim leg to impress on Mike the lack of glamour in faded tennis shoes. "I rather think so. Have you done this before?" She pointed at the sunglasses dangling from his fingers. "You look ready."

"I've done some canoeing, but this is my first time in a raft. What happens if we spring a leak?"

"Then we stop and fix it. Do you think my folks would let us leave without repair kits? There's your life jacket. Don't let Dad see you without it." Lory could have explained in more detail the equipment needed for the expedition, but that could come later. Now the only thing she wanted was to get into a raft with Mike. The past hour had been a whirl of activity with no opportunity for the two of them to do more than smile at each other. Now, however, they were about to shove off.

For the most part, parents and their offspring shared the same rafts, but several of the older children were allowed to pair up in separate rafts. The smallest rafts went to Lory's parents, her youngest brother Brent and his girlfriend, and Mike and Lory. Lory's parents led the way as the group pushed away from the dock and entered the gentle current. Mike had stepped rather tentatively into the lightweight inflated raft, but once he'd settled into the bottom and found firm support for his back on the waist-high side, he reached confidently for the oars. Lory sat facing him, their legs extending into each other's territory. Because of the size of their raft, only one of them at a time would need to man the oars.

"Are you sure you don't want me to row for a while?" Lory asked. "Just until you get the feel of things?"

"Nope," Mike replied jauntily. "I'll take my lumps first thing. You want your nieces and nephews to think your boyfriend can't keep a ten-pound raft on course?"

"Your boyfriend? Where did that come from?" Lory felt safe behind her sunglasses; her eyes wouldn't give away what she was thinking.

"That's what one of the girls called me. The one with the pigtails. What's her name?"

"Angie. Angie's precocious. And a blabbermouth."

"I kind of figured that. She wanted to know if we were going to get married."

"What?" For two cents Lory would have pulled Angie aloft by her pigtails.

"It was a casual conversation. If I recall, she was telling me that she thought Uncle Brent was really going to get married this time. She said something about that only leaving Aunt Lory. The question about my intentions was an afterthought."

"Oh." Lory mulled that over for a moment. "I hope it didn't bother you."

"Nope. I asked her when she was going to get married."

Lory laughed at that, but a little concern surfaced to temper her laughter. Mike had deliberately sidestepped the question. Because they'd entered the river downstream from her home, Lory wasn't able to show Mike where she lived, but she could point out farming land that had been dry lava soil until sweetened by the Snake's life-giving moisture and, in a quiet cove, the beaver dam that had been there longer than anyone remembered.

As the sun started to give off warmth, Lory lost her initial nervousness. True, she could feel Mike's warmth along the full length of her legs and know he was feeling the same thing. True, their sunglasses hid a great deal. But between learning the tricks of keeping a lightweight craft on course, keeping an eye out for the antics of the youngsters ahead of them and trying to pay attention to what she was telling him about their surroundings, Mike had his hands full.

Lory removed her life jacket long enough to shed her sweatshirt and then stretched her arms along the raft's side. Although they'd only been in the water a half hour, she was relaxed. Mike had an instinct for the river; his arms moved in tune with its rhythm. He knew to keep to the center to avoid currents that might draw him close to the bank. His arms moved with slow, sure strength, guiding their craft along its relentless course. In a few miles they would come to a series of rapids, but for now there was little for him to do except keep the raft headed into the flow.

"I could get addicted to this," Mike observed after Lory pointed out several water birds skimming the surface. The raft bucked and rolled, molding itself to the current. "No one can reach us here. I keep thinking, here's all these people and yet we're cut off from the rest of the world."

"It can be deceptive," Lory pointed out. "In the spring, if there's been a heavy snow, the runoff changes things. Then the Snake becomes deeper, faster. It's never a river to be taken for granted."

"I'll take your word for it. You've done this all your life?"

Lory nodded.

"And you don't get tired of it? You're not afraid of it?"

"I don't think I've ever been afraid of the Snake," Lory explained. She changed position, not trying to avoid contact with Mike's legs. "I believe if you have respect for something there's no need for fear. I haven't had much chance to do this in recent years, Mike. You know what my summers are like." She leaned back and arched her neck to catch the sun's rays. Mike was right. No one could reach them here. "Eat your heart out, Keith. This is living."

When she straightened, Mike was still rowing but staring at her legs. "You're getting a tan," he said when she brought questioning eyes to his face.

"I try. It isn't easy."

"I thought about that, about having to spend so much time in jeans."

That had concerned him? "That's one of the few ways I have of pampering myself. I might not get into a beauty parlor all summer, but at least I don't have to look like something left over from last winter."

"You'll never be that, Lory."

Neither of them had brought up last night's conversation. But, awesome as it was, there was only so much they could say about the Snake. Now, maybe, the time they'd spoken about in the dark had come. "Pale legs bother me," Lory laughed at herself. "I also hate having my hair in my eyes and too tight clothes."

"What do you like?"

That was easy. "I love fresh air, watching the sun rise and set, evenings spent with the hotshot crew after a day on the fire line, long showers—my mother's cooking. She's much better at it than I could ever be," Lory confessed. "Do you cook?"

"If there's no way out of it," Mike explained, and then went on to tell her about an abortive cooking class he'd taken in high school. It hadn't been his idea, but the electronics elective he wanted was already filled by the time he registered. "That was the only class I ever got a C in."

"Your only C. That's disgusting." Mike's arms were moving with a rhythm as natural as their conversation. There was, however, a difference. Lory might be casual about the conversation; she could never be casual about the fine interplay of muscle and bone.

Mike wrinkled his nose but stopped when his sunglasses started to slide downward. "I don't tell many people that."

"Because you're embarrassed about taking cooking?"

"Because I don't like tooting my horn about my grades."

For the three hours that it took to reach the spot chosen for the lunch break, Lory and Mike spoke of a hundred things. Their conversation was occasionally interrupted when other rafts drifted near or there were rapids to bounce through, but as soon as each distraction was over, the conversation resumed as if a single beat hadn't been taken.

For years Lory hadn't thought about her abortive attempt to build a Huck Finn raft only to have it sink when she finally dragged it into the water, but she shared that experience with Mike. He countered by admitting that the first time he'd lifted a helicopter off the ground, it hadn't been with the owner's knowledge.

They had both lived alone off campus while going to college and had been so busy with part-time jobs and study that there had been almost no time for socializing. Lory had hated the housekeeping jobs that had been all she could juggle around her classes; Mike had felt the same about his stint as a pizza delivery man. They had both felt challenged by psychology, tolerated biology and excelled in PE. Although they subscribed to separate professional journals, they both received national news magazines that remained unread during the busy summer months.

Mike was trying to work up interest in tackling the needed repairs on the place he'd bought last year. He'd read a couple of books on home repairs; he just hadn't gotten around to doing anything. Lory was already an expert at putting in carpet and storm windows. Lory had taken auto mechanics, not because she enjoyed working on her car, but because she hadn't wanted to take a chance on getting stuck out in the middle of nowhere. Even before he was old enough to drive legally, Mike had taken over maintenance of his mother's cars.

When they stopped for lunch, Lory felt no hesitancy about taking Mike's hand as she stepped out of the raft. Although she was perfectly capable of pulling the raft out of the water, she stood back and let Mike handle that. It wasn't often that Lory let a man take over a task she could handle, but Lory had nothing to prove around Mike. He knew she was capable; it wasn't necessary to repeat the message.

"All that rowing has really worked up my appetite," Mike admitted as Lory handed him a sandwich. "What's in this?"

"Probably everything but the kitchen sink. We got a little carried away."

"Sounds great. However, given what I know about your talents as a chef, maybe I should let you take the first bite."

Lory swiped at Mike, her fingers making contact with his bare chest. With a movement swifter than hers, Mike caught her hand and held it trapped against his bare, sun-warmed flesh. With that contact Lory forgot everything she'd learned about Mike that morning and concentrated on what he was still becoming to her. The warmth her palm absorbed came from the sun, exertion and Mike's body heat. She wanted all that, and more.

Shaken, she looked up to find him staring down at her with an expression that mirrored her own. Now that he'd removed his sunglasses, she was being pulled into crystal lights.

Lory didn't smile; that might have broken the spell. Instead, the hand holding her sandwich dropped heavily to her side, and she slid easily into Mike's one-handed embrace. With three children looking on, Lory lifted her face and found what she'd needed. What she'd been promised last night.

"You do crazy things to me, Ms. Foster," Mike whispered a long minute later.

"It can't be any crazier than what you do to me." Lory ducked her head, not because she was ashamed of what she was saying, but because the gift, which came from her heart, was a new one. "I feel right around you, Mike."

"I've never—"

Mike's tone surprised her. This man, who could pilot massive machinery over a flaming forest, was as unsure as she. Maybe they were ready to talk about a great many things, but they weren't ready for this yet.

At Curt's request, Lory and Mike joined her oldest brother and his wife. Margo had spent the night thinking about some of the things she and Lory had talked about. She was going to take another look at her résumé with an eye to highlighting her recent education. She was going to stop relying on employment agencies, take courage in hand and try to sell herself personally to a firm. Lory listened with half an ear. She was glad that Margo had renewed enthusiasm for her job search, but she and Mike had shared a magical, frightening moment. The spell still swirled around her.

When they reentered the river, Lory suggested she man the oars so that Mike could concentrate on the scenery as they went through a canyon. As he stared up at the steep, lifeless cliffs, she drew a parallel with Hells Canyon. "It's downstream several hundred miles," she explained. "Besides, it isn't the place for a family outing."

"Too swift? I've seen it from the air, but the perspective is different there."

"That's part of it. Mike, you know what the land looks like, how deep the river is. The Snake cuts a mile-and-a-half trench into the Seven Devils Mountains. It's so awesome it's frightening."

"I didn't think anything about the Snake frightened you, Lory."

They weren't going to be able to stay with everyday subjects this afternoon. "A lot of things frighten me, Mike," Lory said without needing to shy from his probing gaze. "I just hope I've learned how to deal with my fears."

"I think you have. I get that sense from you. That's the best any of us can do." He reached out, running his hand over her straining forearm. "Children have their boogeymen. What we fear has substance."

He was right. Utterly right. "War," Lory supplied. "Losing someone we love. Growing old alone." If he hadn't been touching her, Lory would never have admitted that.

Mike leaned back again, but his eyes didn't leave hers. "I don't know if I fear growing old alone. I'm used to being on my own."

"You aren't old yet, Mike," Lory countered. She didn't want this conversation and yet she did. Mike had said he wanted them to get to know each other. Talking about the way they'd paid for their college educations was only a small part of that knowledge. "There are a lot of different ways of being alone." For a minute she stared out at the river, taking strength from its relentless sameness. "If I choose to be alone, that's one thing. But if those I love are taken from me..." She couldn't finish.

Don't do this to me, Lory. I don't want to hear that. Again Mike reached out, touching the soft flesh, feeling the strength that went with it. He was angry at who or whatever had put those words into her mouth. Unreasonably he wanted Lory to come into his life newborn without wounds or scars. "We all lose people we love."

"I know that."

"And I believe we all make certain decisions about how close we're going to allow other people to get." Lory had given him something precious, even if he didn't want it. He had to give her something in return. "I've been doing a lot of thinking about that. Being here, watching your family, has done that to me. Lory, I've always been content with my own company. I didn't ask why that was. It was enough to accept it. But this weekend is showing me an alternative. I think, well, maybe I want to reach out more than I have before."

"Why?"

"Because... I think you know the answer to that."

After they had gone about a half mile from their lunch spot, the river started chasing itself over submerged boulders. Although there was no danger from the rocks, Lory was kept busy negotiating a path through them. When she had a moment to breathe, she gave Mike a quick smile to let him know she had no intention of dumping them. If her smile faltered a little at the end, she couldn't help it.

Let's get to know each other, he'd said. They'd begun the journey. They were in a current of their own. What neither of them could guess was whether they'd be able to navigate through the boulders or crash and be thrown in separate directions.

Squeals from the two closest rafts broke the silent communication. Now that they considered themselves pros, the youngsters were looking for ways to milk the most from their experience. There had been some shifting around during the lunch break so that now the three girls were in one raft while a trio of boys manned another. The sport of the moment was to see who could make the most noise while going through the rapids. Once the river smoothed out again, a game of tag began. First the boys would draw close enough to splash the girls, then the girls would retaliate by ramming the side of the boys' raft.

Lory slowed her craft enough to put distance between them and the high jinks, but it was impossible to hold on to her serious mood when her oldest nephew started beating his chest and yelling Tarzan-like after scoring a direct hit on his now-drenched sister. Laughing, Lory explained that the kids' antics reminded her of her own childhood. "It really was survival of the fittest."

Mike joined in the laughter. None of the adults felt compelled to put the brakes on the youngsters. Far from becoming irritated at their boundless energy, Mike was absorbing their energy, sloughing off his years. Indicating that Lory should pull closer to the boys' raft, he reached for the plastic bucket used for bailing water and a minute later hurtled a full blast in the oldest boy's face.

After that the chase was on. By the time the afternoon's trek was over, Mike had lost his baseball cap, and even Lory's parents were soaked. Mike spent half his time trying to drench anyone who ventured near and the rest bailing water out of their raft. He didn't give up the hopeless task until Lory aimed them toward shore and he leaned out to snag a hunk of lava.

Pushing his wet hair out of his eyes, Mike helped Lory out. Before she could get away, he brought her against him. Lory tried to shake her dripping hair to splash even more water on him, but Mike stopped her. Their wet bodies fused together, lips met. Neither of them gave a thought to the safety of their craft until one of Lory's brothers yelled that it was slipping back into the river.

"Later," Mike promised. A hand slid down her back.

After emptying the rafts, making necessary repairs and setting up their campsite, the Foster clan settled down for a picnic dinner. Lory and Mike sat together to one side of the main gathering. This time they were joined by Brent and his girlfriend. Although Lisa had begun the day with freshly styled hair, it was now plastered against her scalp, accenting her round face. Lisa didn't seem to mind. In a quiet voice she explained that she had been apprehensive about the trip, but now wouldn't have missed it for the world. "I'm a desk jockey," she explained. "I do my exercises every morning, but I'm a total klutz. However, I don't think I've embarrassed myself or Brent yet." The smile she gave Lory's youngest brother said as much as any declaration of love could.

"It's hard to retain much sophistication around this gaggle," Lory admitted. She lifted her own straight hair off her temple, aware that Mike was watching her every move. Although it was still warm, someone had started a campfire. In the growing dusk Mike's features were no longer clearly outlined, and yet the sense of him was something she knew as well as she knew her own heartbeat. Without shyness or hesitancy she leaned against him. Mike took her right hand and started to gently massage her fingers. When she questioned what he was doing, he explained that he had to keep her fingers from stiffening up if he was going to get any work out of her the next day.

Brent agreed. Women, he declared, had a certain well-defined usefulness in life. From that he launched into his theory that it was women and not men who should do the physical labor. After all, women lived longer. They were, therefore, designed not to wear out. Conversely it was men who had the greater intellect.

Lisa swallowed that nonsense as long as she could. She tried to dispute Brent's theory with logic, but he remained steadfast in his belief until she started to tickle him. Mike was working the kinks out of Lory's left hand when Brent abruptly got to his feet, pulling Lisa with him. "You're doing crazy things to me, woman," he stage-whispered. "Now you're going to be sorry."

Lisa's smile said that she might be a lot of things tonight, but sorry wasn't one of them. "The kids might be right," Lory observed as Brent and Lisa were swallowed up by the night. "I think that character has finally met his match."

Mike didn't say anything, and Lory let the silence take over. She might have preferred a comfortable, companionable silence, but with Mike's hands making an impact on a great deal more than her fingers, that was impossible. Lory had been sitting between Mike's legs, using his chest as a backrest while he worked on her hands. Once they were alone, Mike relinquished her fingers. He rested his hands lightly on her shoulders, kneading gently until Lory felt herself flowing into the gesture. Her muscles weren't sore; what he was doing to her was a lifetime away from physical therapy. Slowly, steadily, Mike's fingers inched forward. Lory hadn't changed out of her bathing suit. Neither had she felt a need for her sweatshirt.

It was easy, so easy, for him to explore her throat—and lower. She leaned into him, closed her eyes and surrendered. Lory didn't care at all if anyone noticed his fingers inching toward her breasts.

When the first contact was made, she sighed gently. Mike's quick, deepened breathing and a restless twitch of his thigh muscles telegraphed what he was feeling. What was it she'd told him this morning, that she loved fresh air? Tonight she couldn't seem to get enough of it. With his fingers firm on the swell of her breasts, Lory drank deeply of the night breeze. There was nothing more she could ask for in life. This was why she'd picked up the phone and issued her invitation.

"There's more than one way of getting to know each other, Lory," Mike whispered.

"I know." Tonight, maybe, there wouldn't be the pulling away she'd had to suffer through before. Tonight, maybe, they'd both stretch out their hands and hearts and make the contact. "I'm glad you're here."

Mike's fingers began working a path under the fabric of Lory's suit. When she shivered, he spoke. "I wasn't sure I'd ever see you again. I wasn't sure I deserved to."

"I didn't know whether I was doing the right thing." Lory tried to laugh, but it came out as a weak imitation. "I don't know much about chasing men."

"You weren't chasing me," Mike whispered into her ear. He brushed the side of her neck with his lips before continuing. "I never tried to run away."

"It felt that way."

Mike couldn't dispute what Lory was saying. He still didn't understand why he'd placed those earlier barriers between himself and Lory. He prayed that wouldn't happen again, and yet maybe, even now, it was. How could he tell her that he was afraid of what she was now and might become to him? A man shouldn't be afraid of falling in love.

But things were happening so damn fast and were stronger than anything he'd experienced before. "I know it did," he said inadequately. "That was yesterday, Lory. I don't believe in living in the past."

"Where do you want to live?"

Did she really need to ask him that? Weren't his hands pointing the way? He had no doubt that what she was feeling was as intense as his own reaction. Even now her nipples were hardening from something that had nothing to do with their cooling world. Her breathing had deepened and was matching his in cadence.

"Lory," Mike sighed. "You feel so good." He cupped her breasts, ignoring the interference of her bathing suit, ignoring the current that swept his heart along. "All day I asked myself if we'd be doing this tonight." He wasn't going to draw away. They could take a giant step forward, couldn't they?

Lory pressed her back more firmly against Mike's chest. Although she could barely think beyond what he was doing to her, her fingers somehow found his thighs. Power, potent and real, flowed into her. This was insane! How could she sit within a few yards of her family and be oblivious to everything except Mike? And yet it was happening. The older children were still up; their high voices contrasted with the deeper tones of their parents. This was her family, the people she felt closest to in the world.

Tonight they were strangers. Nothing mattered except Mike.

They could follow Brent and Lisa into the night and reach for each other with a need as old and binding as life itself. Their hearts could join the search. Please. Let it happen.

"Lory?"

Her name was being spoken. She needed to respond. Her yes was a weak moan.

"I have to get up."

"What? Mike, what's wrong?"

"That's just the trouble," Mike whispered. "Too much is right. This isn't the place."

Don't do this to me. Not again! Lory wanted desperately to tell Mike that he was wrong. But she'd tried to push their relationship another time and Mike had withdrawn. Tonight, no matter the cost to her heart, she would follow his lead. "Where are you going?"

"For a walk. And maybe a cold swim. Lory," he continued when she leaned away from him, "I want you. Don't ever doubt that. I thought—all day I told myself that we were ready for this. But I've never made love to a woman with her family around. Can you understand that?"

"I . . . think so."

Mike had said he needed to get up. Instead he leaned forward, wrapping his arms around Lory until she was folded against him again. As a distant owl signaled the coming of night, they remained together, sharing something that needed no words.

After a moment, Mike said, "It's me, Lory. I've spent too much of my life alone."

Lory had no alternative but to accept Mike's explanation. She leaned away to free him from her weight, watching as he rose to his feet, sitting there until she could no longer see him. Her body still felt as if it belonged to someone without nerves or muscles as she made her way to the sleeping bag stretched out next to Mike's. She knew he wouldn't come to bed until she was asleep.

MIKE HAD TOLD LORY that he was going to plunge into the river, but once he reached the shore he reconsidered. Yes, his body was alive with Lory's impact on it. But now he had no desire to wash away that impact. Lory was in him; she deserved to remain there.

He squatted on his haunches, picked up a flat rock and threw it sidearm. Had he retained his boyhood skill of being able to skip rocks farther than any of his peers?

"What do you think so far? Think you're going to survive?"

Mike recognized Lory's father's voice. He turned to see the older couple standing a few feet behind him. "Lory calls this a busman's holiday for the two of you. Don't you ever get tired of the river?"

Janet sat down beside him. "We get tired of the constant upkeep on our equipment," she explained. "And there are some guests..." She shot a long-suffering glance at her husband. "But the river? Never. Mike, we run a snowmobile operation at Caribou in the winter, so it's not as if the Snake is our life. Do you ever get tired of flying your helicopter?"

"Never." A low laugh accompanied Mike's admission. "I'm comfortable with the rut I'm in." Was he, or did he need more than he had?

"I'd hardly call what you do a rut," John Foster pointed out as he joined the other two on the ground. "I'd imagine there's a million paper pushers who envy you your freedom."

"I guess." Mike didn't want to talk about his job. He was much more interested in the two people who had shaped the woman he'd spent the day with. "Were you ever a paper pusher?" he asked.

"For what, about eighteen months?" Lory's father turned to his wife for confirmation. "It took me less time than that to decide I'd be a lot happier running my own business. Finding the right business wasn't an easy decision. Would you believe I majored in political science?"

Mike whistled. "No, I wouldn't."

"Hard to believe, isn't it? You know how it is. I was young and restless and certain I had the answers to the world's political ills. If I knew now what I knew when I was eighteen..."

"Amen to that." Mike nodded in understanding. "I was going to shed the hick town I was living in and go see all the bright lights. I was going to work my way up the corporate ladder and make president by the time I was thirty."

"Did you find the bright lights?" Lory's mother asked.

"Yep." Mike shook his head in disgust. "I also found a lot of shadows under those lights. That life-style wasn't for me any more than the corporate ladder was. I wouldn't be eighteen again for all the money in this state. I might not be as smart as I was then, but at least I know myself a lot better now."

"You need to be your own boss?"

"Yes. And I don't need the bright lights. I hardly ever drink and I hate cigarette smoke and I can't stand loud music and the singles scene—I found it pretty sad." Mike wasn't sure he should be telling Lory's parents this, but the night felt right for sharing. "It wasn't right for me."

"It wouldn't be right for Lory, either," John was saying. "Having four older brothers has forced her to see men with all their faults. When she was a child, she thought her brothers and their friends were pretty much pests. Let me tell you, those boys didn't feel the same way. Do you remember the phone calls that girl used to get, Janet? I couldn't count how many dates she turned down."

"She went on a few," Lory's mother pointed out.

"Yeah, but most of the time that was when you talked her into it. She never did run with the pack."

"That used to bother me," Janet said softly. "I always wanted her to have a best friend. She was surrounded by boys. I thought she needed a girl to be close to, but she seemed happy the way things were."

Lory was content. Content with the way she earned her living, the company of family and work associates. Mike used to feel the same way about himself, but he wasn't so sure about his self-imposed isolation anymore. The woman they were talking about was responsible for the change. "She seems to get along well with the people she works with."

"That's one bright girl," Lory's father was saying. "She could be just about anything she put her mind to. We're damn proud of her."

"You have a right to be."

"She's pretty closemouthed about what she makes, but anyone her age who can buy her own place is doing pretty well. I guess that hazard pay's good." Lory's father paused to try his hand at skipping a rock himself and then went on. "There were a lot of hard times when the kids were growing up. A lot of work and financial insecurity, but we raised a pretty self-sufficient bunch. There's not one of them who doesn't know how to work."

"Sometimes I wish Lory wasn't so damn independent."

Mike wasn't shocked by Janet's profanity. What held his attention was the vehemence behind her words. "You think she's too independent?"

Janet was staring out at the river, her legs drawn up against her body. "She's changed this year. She won't talk to us about it."

"Changed? In what way?"

"Some of the spark's gone out of her," Janet said after a moment of silence. "I used to stew about how dangerous her work was, and she'd tell me not to worry. She kept reminding me that we'd raised her to stand on her own two feet, and if she was going to fall, she'd have to do her own picking up. I tried not to let her know how I felt. I don't want my daughter thinking I'm ever scared for her."

Janet slid closer to her husband, but her eyes remained on the river. "It's hard for a mother to let her baby go. I worried myself to death the first summer she fought fires, and I didn't ever want to hear about the smoke jumping, but by the second summer I'd kind of resigned myself to it. Lory loved what she was doing. She was careful and she'd been well trained. I started to relax. And then last summer—something happened. Something that hurt her a great deal. I wish she'd talk to us about it."

Mike, too, was staring at the river. It didn't matter that he could barely see the Snake. He could hear it; the muted rumble went with the shared mood. "What happened last summer?"

"Lory hasn't told you?"

"No," Mike had to admit. "A couple of the men she works with have hinted at something, but she's never told me anything."

"See?" Janet turned toward her husband. "That girl! Keeping things to herself. She needs to cry, John. If her mother can't get her to, who can?"

Mike needed to know why Lory needed to cry, but if he said anything more, he would be admitting how little he knew about their daughter. "Maybe she's been able to confide with someone at work."

"Maybe having a fire fighter killed—I don't expect Lory to get over that right away—but a mother knows when her baby is carrying something around inside her. All I know is that some man named Jeff died fighting a fire. Lory was there when it happened. She isn't the same person she was before that. I don't know," she whispered. "Lory said Jeff was a friend, but the way she acts—maybe he was more."

Jeff. Now at least Mike had a name. But what was he going to do with it? "The accident? Was Lory in danger?"

"How should I know?" Sighing, Janet brought her voice under control. "Don't mind me. I'm still having trouble letting my little girl grow up. She never was one to come crying to her mother. I probably wouldn't like it if she did. But I just wish there was more I could do."

"You're here." John Foster pulled his wife against his side. "That's all we can do."

"What I wish—" Janet turned toward Mike "—is to have my daughter in another line of work. Why does she have to be a fire fighter?"

"Come on, Mother," John warned. "You know you're proud of her. You brag to everyone who'll listen about how she's turned out."

Janet was still looking at Mike, drawing him into the conversation. "Of course I'm proud of her. But she's turning me into an old woman before my time with this job of hers. I want her safe. Is that too much to ask for?"

"Probably," Mike said, even though it wasn't his place to say that. "Lory's going to do what feels right for her regardless of what anyone wants."

"Don't I know that." Janet leaned against her husband again. "Let me ask you something, Mike. If you and Lory were to get married, would you want her to continue doing what she's doing?"

Mike had never asked himself that question. Lory was who she was, just as he'd come into the relationship fully formed. He couldn't see himself as Lory's husband—not yet.

That wasn't the important issue. Asking Lory about Jeff was.

Chapter Nine

By the time Mike joined Lory, she was already asleep. For a long time he lay next to her, listening to the night sounds. He'd come to bed full of questions, but now he was thinking of nothing save the inroads she'd made on his life. Admitting her power, her control, was both unsettling and exciting. Unsettling because he didn't know what to do with the changes she was bringing to him. Exciting because it was time for his self-imposed silence to become a thing of the past. What lay ahead of them he didn't know. After a while, Mike fell asleep, and when he woke she was already up.

The clan took its time getting ready for the day's journey. It was as if the dictates of time didn't concern any of them, not even John Foster. In the end it was the restless youngsters who herded their elders into the rafts and insisted on shoving off. Lory had been quiet, but when she settled herself in the raft and Mike was walking out to waist-deep water before climbing in himself, her eyes were for him alone. Last night was behind them. She wasn't going to let it color today.

"The landscape's more desolate here," she explained. "The first time I came here I couldn't believe the contrasts. I kept thinking there should be some way to spread the Snake over the ground so something would grow the way it has in the agricultural areas." Lory held the raft steady while

Mike slid in. "There's nothing but lava plains here. Besides, this earth of ours needs a balance."

"I didn't know you majored in philosophy."

"Indulge me. I'm working on world philosophy this morning."

"Sounds impressive."

"What it sounds is presumptuous. How did you sleep?"

Mike didn't answer right away. Finally, though, there was nothing to give her but the truth. "When I did sleep, I stayed asleep."

Lory could have taken the conversation in another direction, but she didn't feel the need. "I wish we were here alone," she said softly. "I love my family but—"

"I had a long talk with your parents after you went to bed."

Lory glanced at the steep-sided cliffs now rising on both sides of them, but the stark, harsh landscape didn't distract her from the meaning behind Mike's simple statement. She had been the subject of that conversation. "Do you want to tell me about it?"

Mike let go of an oar long enough to run his hand up Lory's outstretched leg. "Do you want to hear about it?"

"You covered more than the way I was always whacking off my hair when I was younger, didn't you?" Mike had gone back to the task of keeping the raft on course. Lory thought about returning his gesture by touching his leg, but if he responded the way she had, they might wind up against the rocks.

"You might say that." Mike's eyes strayed to the lifeless cliff. "I'm used to seeing forest," he went on. "Does anything live out here?"

"Eagles. Hawks. Rabbits and coyotes. What did they say, Mike?"

"They're proud of you. They're proud of all their kids."

Lory could laugh at that. "So I've heard. They didn't happen to tell you about the time my brothers tried to sell me, did they?"

Mike leaned back, trying to see to the top of the cliff. "I'm sure I would have remembered if it had come up. How much were they asking?"

Lory's laugh continued. "I think I was going for a couple of dirt bikes, but maybe it was just one and spare tires. My folks didn't take the transaction nearly as seriously as the rest of us did."

Once again Mike took a moment to rest his hand on Lory's knee. When she covered his fingers with her own warm hand, he went on. "They take being parents seriously, Lory."

"I know they do."

"I think they see you as special."

The stretch of river they were going through was deeply shadowed because the sun wasn't yet high enough in the sky to make its impact on the narrow strip of movement in the desolate landscape. But Lory felt no chill. As long as she and Mike were talking, as long as they touched, she would be warm. "That's because they've finally kicked the baby out of the nest. Now they can start to relax."

"It's more than that and you know it. Your father envies you. Something tells me he'd like to give fire fighting a try."

Lory thought about telling Mike about her father's aversion to flying, but that wasn't what the conversation was about. She had to relinquish his hand so that he could go back to rowing, but touching wasn't the only communication open to them. "I don't think anything I'd do would surprise him."

"Probably not." Because they'd just come out of a bend in the river, Mike was able to focus on Lory once again. "Have you ever talked to your mother about how she feels?"

So this was what the conversation was about. "Not really. I don't see that much of them these days, and when I do there's always someone else around. What did she tell you?"

"Are you sure you really want to hear this?"

Lory frowned. She couldn't imagine anything that serious had been said. "I think I'm going to hear it no matter what I say."

"What you do scares her, Lory. She thinks about the dangers."

Lory didn't want her mother to be frightened. If it was within her power to do so, she'd never give her parents a moment of concern, but in the real, unpredictable world that wasn't possible. "She's never told me that."

"I didn't think she had."

The cliffs were falling away, letting more sunlight onto the river. Lory reached for her sunglasses, but didn't take her eyes off Mike. It struck her as a sad but undeniable fact that parents and children had to chart a careful course in their relationship with each other. Lory wanted to give her parents no cause for concern. At the same time, she suspected, they kept as much of their aging as possible from her. "I wish she wouldn't worry."

Mike was caught up in something that, maybe, had nothing to do with what she'd just said. Lory could sense his preoccupation, but didn't know how to break through it. She wished she could simply accept that her parents had revealed things to him that they kept from her, but she couldn't. Did they see Mike as someone who was already part of their lives? "What did she say?" she asked when there was nowhere else for her thoughts to take her. "Is there anything I can do?"

"Probably not." The landscape had leveled out and become lava flats again. The youngsters had become bored with their surroundings and were playing an elaborate game of follow the leader. Although he was encouraged to join in,

Mike hung back, giving him and Lory privacy. "I don't think your mother would like that, either. She doesn't want to influence your life."

"But she does," Lory moaned. "I love her. I love both of them. I don't want them to worry."

Mike drew on the oars, slowing the craft even more so that there was no danger of anyone hearing what he had to say. "They can't help it, Lory. You told them about Jeff."

"So that's it," she said on the tail of a long, slow breath. "Mom thinks what happened to Jeff might happen to me."

"It could, Lory."

"I know that. Every fire fighter knows the risk is there. But, Mike, you know about helicopter crashes. That hasn't stopped you from flying."

Before she knew he was going to do it, Mike gripped her ankle. His touch on her leg a few minutes ago had been a message of tenderness and communication, but now there was something—anger maybe—in the gesture. "Don't try to minimize the risk, Lory. I'm above a fire. You're on the line."

"I know what I'm doing. I'm not going to get killed."

"Jeff was killed."

Jeff was killed. How brutally simple the words were. But Mike didn't know the whole story, and until she'd found the courage to tell him, she couldn't expect him to understand. "I know that."

"Then you know why your mother worries."

Mike released her ankle, giving Lory the freedom to breathe. "Tell me something, Mike. Can you really talk to your mother? No," she said, stopping him when he started to speak. "I know you can talk to her about your job and your house and the California Angels. I understand how close the two of you were when you were growing up. But let me ask you something, if you've ever felt lonely or scared, would you be able to tell her?"

"That's a hell of a question to ask, Lory."

"It's no harder than what you're asking me to do. I'm not going to tell my mother about the times on the fire line when I'm not sure I'm going to get out of there. And you're not going to tell your mother what it feels like to spend half your life alone in the cockpit of a helicopter fighting destruction that doesn't have to happen."

"All right," Mike said after a silence that seemed to stretch across the flats and snag itself on distant, jagged rocks. "You've made your point. Neither of us can tell our mothers certain things. But—" his eyes bored into hers and gave Lory nowhere to escape to "—you have to tell someone."

"Do I?"

"Yeah, you do. I remember something you said the day I met you. You were talking to that reporter. He asked what you'd do if your husband wanted you to change jobs. You told him you wouldn't marry any man who didn't understand you. Did you mean that?"

"Yes."

"Then some day you're going to have to tell a man what's going on inside here." Mike tapped her forehead. "And here." His hand found her left breast and lingered over her heart. "Maybe that's why you haven't gotten married, because you keep it all inside."

"That isn't fair!" Shocked by her outburst, Lory looked around, but no one was looking at them. "I don't keep everything inside."

"You haven't told me about being afraid."

God! Why was he doing this to her! And yet Lory couldn't blame Mike. They were saying things she'd said only once before in her life. Starting up again took more courage than maybe she had. "I told Jeff."

"Jeff's dead. He can't help you."

"I know that. Don't push it, Mike."

"Why? Because I'm not the right one?"

"What are you doing to me?" Lory moaned. "I asked you to spend the weekend with me. I've never asked a man to do that before." She could have stopped with that, but Mike had pushed. She was going to push back. "You closed up like a clam when we were at the motel. If I'd listened to your message, if I didn't want to give it another try, I would have waited for you to call me. When would that be, Mike? Would you have ever gotten in touch?"

Mike chose to ignore her last question. "You're upset."

"You're damn right I'm upset. You're accusing me of not being open. It works both ways, Mike."

"I'd say we're both being pretty open right now."

Mike was right. Lory had already had that thought, but it took Mike saying it for her to see how far they'd come. "It has to happen, Mike," she agreed. "I just hope we don't wind up wanting to drown each other before it's over."

I don't think that's going to happen, Mike thought. He wanted to point out that Lory hadn't said enough. He knew almost nothing more about Jeff than he had last night, but they were both stepping into territory they'd never traveled before. To succeed, the journey had to be a slow one. "Do you know what I think is the problem in your family?"

"I wasn't aware that we had any problems."

"Everyone does. All of you have so much fun together that the conversation never goes past that."

"You don't know what you're talking about, Mike."

"Don't I?"

"All right. Maybe you have a point. What do you suggest?" To his relief, Lory was smiling. "Would you like my mother and me to duke it out the way you and I have been doing?"

"It might be better than all this sweetness I'm hearing," Mike said, although the strong, loving current in the Foster family was what made it special. "I didn't mean it. I'm glad your family gets along as well as it does, but you're not leaving the door open for spilling your guts."

Although they were being pulled along by a swift current, Lory wasn't being distracted. "Who made you a psychiatrist?"

"I did. I specialize in patching up relationships."

"You're doing a damn good job of it." Lory's smile blunted her clipped words. "Mike, it wasn't easy for me to tell my mother how I feel about my job. I don't want her to worry."

"Worry goes with the territory. You worry about your parents, don't you?"

"You know I do."

"Then don't deprive them of the same emotion. You're a caring person, Lory." Although the current kept him from touching her, he hoped that what he was sending her served the same purpose. "If you've told one person, if you've told Jeff, you can tell another."

"What am I going to tell them?"

"Anything. Everything. Lory, your mother worries that you keep too much inside. I agree. Your parents don't know how Jeff's death has affected you. That can't be the only thing."

"It isn't."

"Then tell them."

The conversation drifted off into other directions for the rest of the morning, but what had been said stayed with Mike. Mike had never considered himself intuitive. He'd often felt at a disadvantage when it came to relationships. But he'd been able to pinpoint what Lory and her mother needed to work on.

Just as he now knew that the time would come when Lory would tell him about Jeff.

LORY HELD CENTER STAGE during the after-dinner conversation. In the beginning it was an effort because Lory was accustomed to letting her brothers run roughshod over her. But she'd spent years listening to their accomplishments. Now it was time for them to do the listening. With Mike sitting next to her, she waited for her opening and then began. "You have it easy," she said in response to something her second eldest brother had just said about the difficulty of being a foreman with management on one side of an issue and the workers exerting like pressure on him. "All you have to deal with are twenty or thirty people."

"What do you know?" James shot back. "You're out there in the middle of the woods all the time. The deer or whatever you bump into can't talk back."

Lory snorted her reaction to that comment. "Try a balancing act between loggers and conservationists. Half of them want access to the forests so they can make a living from them. The other half wants to put up a brick wall and keep us all out."

When James pointed out that that was an exaggeration, Lory posed a question. "What would you do if you were under pressure to allow leases for geothermal exploration while at the same time you were told that the exploration could adversely affect Yellowstone's geyser basin? You decide. Do you want to tap a potential energy source, or are you going to hold off to protect a national park?"

James tried to make the point that it wasn't Lory's decision, but she countered with one she had been instrumental in making. Each year different Oregon forest lands had their roads closed to protect the elk herds. Despite pressure from hunting concerns, Lory, representing the forest service, held firm. She'd attended several forums called by hunters and weathered their questions, accusations and complaints. "It's impossible to please everyone. Believe me, I know."

Lory's mother expressed concern over Lory being placed in the position of having to defend forest-service policies, but Lory had been doing so for enough years that it no longer bothered her. However, it hadn't always been so. "You should have seen me the first time I had to defend the amount of old growth timber that would be allowed to remain in an area to an environmental group. I was shaking so badly I couldn't read any of the figures I'd been given. But don't worry, Mom. Thanks to those brothers of mine, I know how to duke it out with the best of them. And, thanks to them, not even a firestorm frightens me. I know what I'm doing out there. That's why they let me fight forest fires."

"That's something I've never been able to figure out," James said. "What got you interested in doing that in the first place?"

Surprised and pleased by her brother's interest, she explained, as best she could, about the rush that came from being presented with a challenge. "Why does anyone climb a mountain? Because it's there."

"You fight a fire because it's there?"

"Basically." Lory nodded. "And because I refuse to let anything intimidate me."

Janet needed to have Lory repeat her last statement, but by the time the conversation turned to other matters, Lory believed she'd made her point. That belief was reinforced when, as the evening drew to a close, Mike ran his lips over her cheek.

"That's the way, kid," he whispered. "What'd I tell you? Getting that herd to listen to you isn't so hard, is it?"

"No, it isn't," Lory whispered. "I guess I just never thought they'd be that interested."

"I'm interested. Why shouldn't your family be?"

"Because..." Lory struggled to hold on to her thoughts despite the distractions of Mike's breath on her neck, and his arm resting lightly on her hip. "I guess I still think of myself as the tagalong when I'm around my family. I regress when I'm surrounded by them."

"Make that past tense. You know something, woman? I've been sitting a long time."

Lory knew what Mike was saying. It was time for them to be alone.

Silently Lory followed Mike to the flat area where they'd left their sleeping bags. Wordlessly Mike released her hand and picked up the down-filled bags. When he once again put them on the ground, they were a good hundred yards away and out of sight of the rest of the group. Lory dropped to her knees and began pulling her bag out of its nylon covering. She wanted to ask Mike if tonight was going to be different, and yet the moment didn't feel right for words. She reached for Mike's hand, smiling at him in the dark.

Mike, too, had spread out his sleeping bag. After releasing Lory's hand, he stretched out on it, propped himself up on one elbow and patted the space in front of him. She had yet to settle herself near him when she spoke. "Jeff would have been proud of me. You would have liked him."

"Tell me about Jeff. Please."

"Jeff's dead, Mike."

"I know he is. But he lives in your heart. I'd like to think I have a right to know about him."

"You do," Lory whispered. She turned onto her back and stared up at the night. Ten thousand stars looked down at her, waiting for the moon to join them, warming her. "Jeff was my best friend."

"Did you love him?"

Lory sensed hesitancy in Mike. Maybe he was afraid of opening old wounds. If that was the case, Lory loved him for his sensitivity, but she was ready to talk about Jeff. "Of course I did," she answered softly. "He was a special man."

"How special?"

Lory could sense Mike watching her, but if she were to succeed at telling him about someone and something that had changed her life, she would have to bury herself in last summer. "Have you ever known someone you could tell things to that you've never told another human being?" Lory glanced at Mike but went on before he could give her an answer.

"That's the way it was with Jeff and me. The things I told my family earlier this evening? Jeff knew about them and a thousand other things. Mike, I told him things I never knew I wanted to tell anyone until he came into my life. The first time I had a shouting match with a hunter I called Jeff and talked until I'd calmed down. He was the one to give me the boost that resulted in my becoming involved in arson investigation. I'd been talking about it for months. It was Jeff who told me to put my money where my mouth was. It's hard to explain." Once again Lory glanced at Mike, finding the depths of his hazel eyes despite the pinpricks of light. "I think what it all boiled down to was, Jeff and I could be honest around each other."

Mike reached out with his free hand and traced the outline of Lory's lips with feathering fingers. "Were you there when he died?"

Lory nodded. She'd been over that night so many times that it shouldn't cause her pain. And yet it did. Maybe, this time, it was because she was sharing the past with someone who was part of her present, and maybe her future. "We'd been on the fire line for three or four days. The crews were thinly stretched because there had been a lot of lightning strikes. We hadn't had enough sleep. None of us were as clearheaded as we should have been, but Jeff—" This time when Lory found Mike's face, her eyes stayed on him. What she felt for the two men was different, and yet there was an essential sameness. They were both men she could be honest with. "I wonder if the memory will ever fade? It seems like yesterday."

Mike leaned over Lory, replacing his fingers with his mouth. Her lips were unbelievably sweet, unbelievably ready for him. He wanted to replace words with gestures, but that would only leave things unfinished. "I'd like to know."

Lory nodded, her eyes focused on his mouth, only a few inches away. "I want to tell you." It was her turn to commit his lips to memory by running the tips of her fingers over them. "I think—what has made it so hard for me to talk about Jeff is my guilt."

"What do you have to feel guilty about?"

Lory had to close her eyes to concentrate. They had done right by going off by themselves to talk, but having Mike so close with his compassion and caring flowing over her was making thought difficult. "I could have stopped Jeff. I should have found a way to keep him with me."

Mike didn't say anything. Instead he took her hand in his and held it against his mouth. His kisses, quick little whispers of emotion, gave more than a thousand words. Lory had Mike's strength now. She could say the rest.

"I'd never seen Jeff that hurt before. Mike, he was a seasoned fire fighter. He knew what we were up against. He'd been asked to go on working no matter how tired he was— he should have been able to handle it—but he'd never had a woman hurt him like that before."

Something deeper replaced the concern on Mike's face. He dropped her hand only to replace that contact with one that made it even harder for Lory to concentrate. Now he was testing the pulse at her throat, his breath flowing over the sensitive skin there. "I don't understand," he whispered.

"Jeff was in love," Lory explained despite the distraction of Mike's presence. "He'd bought her a ring the week before. But she wouldn't take it. She didn't want to be engaged to someone who was gone all the time, who might not come back to her."

"Jeff tried to give a ring to someone else. What about you?"

"What do you mean, what about me?" Didn't Mike know what his fingers on her throat were doing to her? How could he expect her to think? "It was Jeff's life. It didn't have anything to do with me."

"You weren't in love with Jeff?"

"Oh, Mike." Lory turned toward Mike, her eyes wide with understanding. "You thought ..."

Lory could see Mike's throat working. His eyes had grown wary and questioning, but at least he was still touching her. "You said you loved him."

"I did," Lory tried to explain. "But, Mike, I wasn't in love with him. Jeff took chances with his physical safety because his mind was on a woman, but I wasn't that woman."

Mike let his breath out in a harsh sigh. "You and Jeff weren't in love?"

"No." It might not be safe for her to try to touch Mike now, but Lory couldn't help herself. She lifted her arms from where they'd been resting lightly on her stomach and encompassed Mike's neck. Her reward came in his lack of resistance as she drew him closer. "Mike, Jeff was my friend. He was the best friend I've ever had, but I didn't love him. At least it wasn't the kind of love you're talking about."

Mike understood her. His lips strong and possessive on hers were the only explanation Lory needed. There were a thousand things she could tell Mike about the special closeness she and Jeff had shared, but this wasn't the time. Mike was someone Jeff had never been for her. It was that emotion that Lory now needed to explore.

"Do you think anyone has noticed that we're not where we started the evening?" she asked.

"I don't think it's any of their business," Mike answered before putting an end to words. He leaned over Lory, trapping her between his arms. Not that Lory felt trapped. His strength over her was everything she needed. She helped make the contact, instantly turning a soft, questioning kiss into something hungry and alive. With that kiss, Lory was no longer a woman interested in divulging the past.

The past had had its say. It was now time for the present.

Mike lowered himself until his elbows were bearing the weight of his upper body, which freed his hands to play with Lory's hair. "I love your hair," he whispered. "It's so soft."

"It smells like the river."

"I like that, too. Lory, you're a part of your surroundings. I look at you and see a woman who can jump out of bed and be ready to go in seconds."

"Would it ruin your image of me if I told you about my addiction to coffee? My brain doesn't engage until I've had a cup."

"But your instinct works." Mike was testing a theory. If he kept his lips inches from Lory's would she be able to concentrate, or would she act on instinct? "You've been fighting fires for so long that you could do it in your sleep."

"I could?" Lory's whisper was softer than it had been a minute ago. "What about you? Could you—"

"Could I what?"

"I don't remember." Lory tightened her hold on Mike's neck. "I don't remember what I was going to say."

"You don't have to say anything. Neither of us do." Mike sat upright. Lory's hands slid from his neck to his chest, catching at the buttons of his shirt. His eyes said all that needed to be said.

Lory didn't take lovemaking lightly. It was, she believed, an act of utmost faith and trust. Exposing one's body, mind and soul to another called for total surrender. That surrender would never take place if either partner was unable to give completely.

Tonight Lory was ready for the ultimate test of giving. She'd already opened her mind to him. Her body now lay waiting. And if it was right—if everything was perfect—their hearts might join as well.

That question could wait until later. Lory shivered as Mike made the first gentle exploration of the flesh exposed by her blouse's V. For a moment she lay quiet, wondering at the wisdom of showing him what two days together had done to her. But as his hand dipped lower, Lory made a decision that would frame the night. They had only this weekend. Neither of them had said anything that might go beyond that time.

Lory would take tonight for everything it could be. Maybe Mike would understand that tonight wasn't enough, and maybe their future meant nothing to him. She couldn't be responsible for the future. All she could deal with was tonight.

Lory wasn't going to wait. She needed to feel his body under her fingers. She needed to know if the potential was as great as she believed. Her fingers were firm as she pulled his T-shirt out from under his jeans and pulled the fabric upward.

"I thought we came here to talk," Mike whispered. He was arching away from her touch, but not trying to break free.

"Do you want to talk?" Lory could have tried to pretend she wasn't reacting to his nearness, but something would have given her away. Instead she let her actions telegraph everything. She lifted her back off the sleeping bag, bringing herself closer to him.

"No." His lips were almost on hers; just the sense of them took away all thought. "Don't talk. Not now."

"I won't," she promised him.

Mike was magic. He understood more about her body than she ever had. Although Lory struggled to remember to bring Mike pleasure, she was lost in her body's potential and the keys that were unlocking that potential. She was back out on the river, only this time she needed no raft to keep her afloat. The current—Mike's current—had her in its grip. Fighting it was impossible; wanting to fight unthinkable.

It mattered not at all that they were sharing this corner of the wilderness. When Mike helped her out of her blouse, Lory had no need for clothing, modesty or thoughts that went beyond what was taking place on their sleeping bags. She forced her muscles to respond long enough to remove Mike's shirt and obeyed his prompting when her fingers fumbled with his zipper. He was much more sure of himself, or so Lory thought until his breath turned ragged.

The knowledge filled Lory with fresh wonder. Hers wasn't the soft, pampered body of a woman who gave thought to her looks, and yet Mike wanted what she was.

That she wanted him was a given. Why else would she feel so bold as to run her hands down his naked thighs, spread her fingers over his flat belly? Despite the sharp whiskers shadowing him, her lips couldn't get enough of his mouth. That was only the beginning. Lory wouldn't be complete until every inch of her flesh had felt every inch of him. It mattered not at all how long that would take. She had the rest of her life. He was, without reservation, her everything.

They lay naked on the sleeping bags, bodies ready. Mike worked his tongue over Lory's breast, bringing her ever closer to the moment when she would no longer know or care who she was. Her hands were small rivers of quicksilver eager to leave their imprint. Lory turned toward him, opening her eyes for the first time in long minutes. The question didn't need to be asked; the acquiescence needed no words. Becoming Mike's lover was the only thing she wanted out of life.

"No second thoughts?"

"I want you," Lory said without shame.

"I've never pressured a woman. If you feel I have—"

"Don't say it, Mike," Lory stopped him. "Can't you tell what you're doing to me? There's no question."

"You want me?"

Do I want to go on living? Lory could have given him that as her answer, but she could give him something better than words. She reached for him; her body was molten lava, needing even more fire before the flame could be extinguished. Mike had given her everything and yet it wasn't enough. The ultimate inferno would come only when their bodies became one.

He understands, Lory thought as Mike lifted himself over her.

Lory was losing herself. A moment ago she'd been a woman reacting to the man who'd become the most important thing in her life. But the line between who she was and what he'd become blurred. That Mike wanted to make love to her, Lory took as the ultimate gift of faith. He'd been complete within his powerful helicopter. He could have spent his life in proud mastery of the world he'd created, but he'd come to her.

Given himself to her.

And all she had to give in return was herself.

Later, in the middle of the night, Lory finished the story that had brought them to this place. Jeff, she believed, would have been alive if he hadn't fallen in love. With her lover holding her secure against him, Lory described the night when her best friend hadn't been able to listen to her loving logic. Jeff's mind hadn't been on the fire. He couldn't get a woman out of his mind. No matter what Lory tried to tell him, it all came back to one simple fact: the woman he loved was no longer part of Jeff's world, and without her, his life didn't mean enough. Lory tried to call him back into the pocket of safety the fire fighters had created, but the night was calling him. He needed to be alone to think.

Jeff got his aloneness. A lifetime of aloneness.

With her head resting on Mike's chest, Lory cried. She hadn't allowed herself to shed tears since Jeff's funeral, telling herself that tears wouldn't bring her friend back. But because her own life now had a definition it never had before, she was finally able to whisper the farewell that had been too much to face before.

Jeff, her best friend, was no longer part of her existence. But Mike had brought back the sunlight.

"We could talk about everything," Lory whispered into Mike's chest. "I wouldn't let myself admit how much I've missed that."

"What about the people at work? Your family?"

Lory shook her head. "It was special with Jeff and me." She held back, waiting for grief to subside. "I could be open with him."

"That doesn't sound like a friend. It sounds like a lover."

Casting off what she still felt for Jeff, Lory concentrated on Mike. "I had a man for a best friend, Mike. I want you to believe that."

"I do." Mike kissed her long and soft to reinforce what he'd just said. He didn't tell her that he felt as if he were standing on the outside because Lory and Jeff had shared something he'd never experienced. What he could do was turn a comforting touch into what he and Lory did share.

Her reaction was so fast, so honest. Mike had never had a woman ready to give so totally of herself. He'd never lost himself in a woman before. Never given up everything. Never looked love in the face.

Love? Mike tried to distance himself from the word, to hold it in his hand and study it, but he was too close to the emotion.

Lory trusted him with her body and maybe her heart, as well. He could think that because his own heart was on a journey it had never before taken. He didn't want to believe he was the only one on that journey. Yes, he would take her giving tonight, accept what was happening to him and make the night pure and good. He could feel more than he'd ever felt in his life, ever known it was possible to feel.

But no matter what was happening to him that didn't give him any answers for tomorrow.

Mike had never been asked to share his tomorrows with anyone before. Never been in a woman's hands. Never had love sweep over him.

That scared him.

Once again Lory was losing herself. The competent woman who'd always been in control had been snuffed out. Mike's hands, his body, had extinguished her and left in the wake of that wreckage a woman who needed and wanted nothing but to be loved by Mike Steen.

Love. Lory didn't try to deny or turn away from what was more emotion than word. Here, with Mike defining her world, there was no questioning what had taken place along with the lovemaking. With the Snake providing the music to go with the word, Lory faced what she'd never asked herself to face before.

Falling in love had never happened. She'd never guessed it could be so complete. Never guessed she would want a man as much as she wanted Mike tonight—and for the rest of her life.

And that scared her.

Chapter Ten

Lory was standing beside a government-green vehicle in a wilderness area some fifteen miles from Wallace in northern Idaho. Although the region was known primarily for its lead and silver mining, Lory had been called into the Clearwater Mountains to investigate a burn that logic said shouldn't have happened. The day was going to be hot, but at a little after dawn the mountains were still cool, insulating Lory from what she'd left behind.

"I didn't figure there was any question about it," her companion said. "But you know how it is when you're working with the government. Everything has to be verified."

Lory nodded in response to what George Scholes was telling her. Although she'd done everything that needed to be done to verify the cause of the small fire on forest service land, she'd sensed from the start that this one had been deliberately set. Not only was the land off limits to recreationists, and government personnel hadn't been in the area for the better part of the summer, but there hadn't been anything resembling a lightning strike in weeks. Still, she held off saying anything until she had proof that the destruction had been caused by two small fires burning together. Two separate, simultaneous fires pointed toward one thing: the twenty-five-acre blaze had been deliberately set.

"Do you know anyone who has something against the government?" she asked. "An ex-employee maybe."

"Maybe. However, let me show you something. Maybe you'll come to the same conclusion I have." George said nothing more but indicated that Lory should get back into the four-wheel-drive vehicle with him. The spare, wiry, middle-aged man headed west of the burn and fifteen minutes later stopped at the top of a high bluff that overlooked miles of wilderness. He handed Lory a powerful pair of binoculars and pointed at a distant spot. "What do you see down there?"

It took Lory only a few seconds to identify a discarded truck, empty gasoline barrels, a length of chain, and most telling, a fresh clearing. "Logging. George, legit operators wouldn't leave that mess."

"And the legit guys aren't working this area. There haven't been any timber sales here. What I'm thinking is, some independent businessmen took a chance that we wouldn't have any reason to come up here for weeks, months, maybe. That gave them time to take their trees and get the hell out."

"And you're thinking—" Lory paused "—that whoever did this had a hand in the burn?"

"Maybe. The only question is, why?"

Lory had been asking herself the same question. Her mind went back to a burn she'd taken a look at earlier. Like this spot, the other area abutted on recently logged acreage. Lory's preliminary investigation had leaned toward a careless fire at an illegal logging operation that would have gotten out of hand if the so-called loggers hadn't pulled out all the stops fighting it, but two such accidents only a few miles apart didn't compute.

Maybe neither fire had been an accident. If two sets of thieves had been in the woods, and if they started fighting over who would get the timber... "Arson," Lory spat out.

"Double arson. Not only are they setting a deliberate fire on government land, but they're trying to wipe out the competition."

George turned serious eyes on Lory. "But how do we prove it? And how do we put an end to it? Those guys aren't going to quit. They're going to keep at each other, letting fires do the threatening. The next fire might cover a hell of a lot more than twenty-five acres. It's got to be stopped."

Lory had several thoughts on how that could be accomplished, but before she could put her plan into action, she needed to talk to the county sheriff's department and local forest-service top brass. After being returned to Wallace, Lory called on the forest area supervisor and then, armed with his promise of cooperation, met with Sheriff R. H. McWilliams. Because she'd worked with R.H. before, Lory was able to get right to the point. She settled herself in his cramped office, stuck out her feet and swept everything except what she was here for from her mind.

"You've got problems, R.H.," she stated. "Just because the forest service has closed this area doesn't mean logs aren't going out of here."

R.H. grunted, his bulk sprawled over the only chair in the county that could handle his 250 pounds of muscle and pizza indulgence. "You think you're telling me something I don't know? It's good to see you, Lory. I thought maybe you'd have gotten married and given up this insane business."

"No on both counts," Lory explained. It had been three days since she and Mike had parted. Three days of doing paperwork, waiting for the next fire call, not hearing from Mike, trying not to think about the words neither of them had said and the love that was still a part of her. She'd jumped at the arson investigation because her mind needed more to do. "Besides, if I got married, what would happen to us?"

"Good question. I'd hate to have to lose you to some man. So? I take it this is about the Gem Valley fire. Any idea who set it?"

It didn't surprise Lory that R.H. had come to the conclusion that the fire wasn't the result of some backfiring vehicle. She'd be surprised if he hadn't already guessed that an illegal activity was involved. Briefly Lory described what she'd seen. "What worries the forest service is that this isn't the first time. I understand it's the third such fire this summer, and with things as dry as they are there's a real potential for a fire getting out of control." She chose her next words carefully, alert to any defensiveness on R.H.'s part. "Short of calling in a SWAT team and having them camp out in the mountains, I don't know how we're going to put a stop to the timber thefts and some pretty violent squabbling over squatters' rights."

"Look, Lory, I've done everything I can, but I simply don't have the manpower. I suggested that the forest service hire someone to fly over their land, but that's not in their budget. They've closed off a few roads, but whoever is going up there takes along wire cutters. They're so far back in the woods that the noise of their machinery doesn't carry. The logs come out at night. There's just too damn many logging roads to keep an eye on them all."

Lory nodded and then made her suggestion. Up until now, both law enforcement and the forest service had concentrated their energies on going after the lawbreakers. But what if she helped bait a hook? "There have to be citizens, maybe hikers or people with off-road vehicles, who have seen something. If they were given an incentive, a reward, they might come forward. The forest service said it would come through with something."

Lory told R.H. that she was willing to make a public appeal before the media and capitalize on her position as an arson investigator. She'd also given thought to putting out word that law enforcement had several leads but needed to substantiate them. "I'm thinking, not only might there be someone out there who knows something, but we might make the loggers nervous enough that they'll make a mistake. Maybe they'll start pointing fingers instead of lighting fires."

R.H. had no objections to Lory's plans, but he did have reservations about the extent of her involvement. He'd been around long enough that he had several suspects. From past experience he knew they'd get both nervous and angry if they thought their "business" was in jeopardy. And if they were nervous enough, they might try to retaliate. "I'm not sure having your face on the news is wise," he stressed. "They're going to see a skinny woman talking about putting them out of business. I think I should be the one—"

"That's precisely why I think I should make the appeal," Lory interrupted. "If they see your mug or feel the weight of the forest service behind this, they'll just wait us out. However—" Lory made a show of fluffing her hair "—if a sweet young thing made an impassioned appeal—"

"You're no sweet young thing," R.H. interrupted. "You're just as crusty as I am."

"Which is precisely why I keep waiting for you," Lory quipped. "Come on, R.H., I've spent the past three days shuffling papers. I'm about to lose my mind." She didn't tell him that paperwork had nothing to do with her mental state.

In the end R.H. agreed. Although he was still concerned about Lory's involvement, he admitted that her appeal to the public's conscience would carry the most weight. Before the day was over, Lory had been interviewed by the local newspaper and contacted a regional TV station that agreed to send someone to take her statement.

That evening Lory went back to her motel room and put in a call to Keith. The hotshot crew had their eyes on a rangefire and were expecting to be deployed at any time.

"I'll let you know when that happens," Keith explained. "If you can join us, fine. But I'll understand if this business keeps you tied up."

Lory had stretched out on her bed while the phone rang. Now she closed her eyes, wanting to be with Keith and the others instead of here, feeling her aloneness. "I'd rather be with you," she said wistfully. "I don't know how long I'll be useful here."

"What's the matter, kid?"

"What?" How had Keith known what she was feeling?

"You're sounding like a kid who got forgotten at Christmas. It can't be the job you're doing because you sound enthusiastic about that. What is it? Hard to come back to work after the weekend?"

"Kinda," Lory hedged.

"Well, don't worry about it. You and Mike will have other weekends."

"I'm not so sure about that." Lory could have kept her thoughts to herself, but she was lonely tonight, which made her talk too much.

"Problems?"

"Maybe. I don't know." Lory tried to divert Keith by telling him about the raft trip, but all that accomplished was opening up emotions better kept under wraps. Finally she convinced Keith that the call was costing them too much and hung up. But the damage had been done. Tonight there weren't any fires to fight or investigate. Tonight there was nothing but the memory of when, once again, she'd had to watch Mike disappear into his helicopter and from there into the sky.

One more goodbye. Lory wasn't sure she could take another. But if she didn't say something, and Mike didn't, either, how could she put an end to the goodbyes? There must be words she could say to let Mike know that their separate life-styles, their independence, weren't compatible with what had happened to her heart. But what if she did and he told her that was the way he wanted it?

Lory slept poorly. In the morning she was interviewed by the TV station and then hung around R.H., making a pest of herself. Together the two of them watched the evening news, commenting on the effectiveness of her appeal. Lory was pleased that she'd been able to interject concern into her short spiel. Overlooking the fact that she'd come across looking like a ninety-pound weakling, she focused on the seriousness of her plea. "I forgot I'd said that about the criminal element jeopardizing everyone's safety. Hopefully that'll make the right impact."

"And it might backfire on you," R.H. pointed out. Before the evening was over, Lory was given a graphic lesson in what the sheriff was talking about. The two of them were still in R.H.'s office when the phone rang. A minute later R.H. handed the receiver to Lory and whispered, "I think we have a nibble, but I don't think this is a civic-minded citizen."

Lory kept her eyes on R.H. as she said hello. "You the lady who was on the TV earlier?" a deep voice asked.

"Yes. If you know something about the fires, you're supposed to talk to the sheriff."

"I know what I'm doing all right. You listening? There aren't any places you can hide in this burg."

Lory stiffened. She arched her eyebrows, indicating concern, but didn't try to answer the question in R.H.'s eyes. "Why should I hide?"

"If I was you, lady, I'd be getting the hell out of this town while I still could."

"Oh?" Lory deliberately kept emotion out of her voice, but her fingers were turning into a tight fist. "Why is that?"

"Because you're too young to die."

Lory paused. The threat didn't bother her as much as deciding on the proper response. If she acted frightened, she might get nothing more from the caller. However, if she made him angry, he might tip his hand. "I don't have any intention of dying. If this is a threat—"

"It's no threat. It's a promise. You're right, lady. There probably is some idiot out there who can point the finger. He'll do it for the reward unless he gets the message that squealing is dangerous to his health."

"And how are you going to get that message to someone you don't know?" Lory asked, although she was fast catching on.

"You." The man laughed his grating laugh. "You're going to get it to him. Look, I know the sheriff's listening, so I'm going to keep it short. You've got two choices. Either you get back in front of the camera, tell everyone there's no reward and hightail it out of town or—"

"Or what?" Lory stared at her fist. A woman who faced raging fires for a living didn't scare that easily.

"You want I should spell it out? Or we make an example of you."

"I'm not the one you have to worry about."

"What the hell do you know? You turn up dead and no one's going to know who to point fingers at. Unless you're stupid, you know what you gotta do." The receiver was slammed down almost before the last words were said.

"Well?" R.H. asked before Lory could hang up the phone. "He was threatening you, wasn't he?"

Lory nodded. She'd been in dangerous situations before, but this was the first time the danger had come from a human. "He thinks either he can scare me off or use my body as a warning to others."

"Damn!" R.H. lurched to his feet. His bulk filled the room, giving Lory a sense of reassurance simply because he was there. "I knew this was going to happen. Didn't I tell you you could wind up in trouble?"

"It's a threat, R.H.," Lory tried to point out. "That's all it is."

"You don't know these people the way I do. Money means a hell of a lot more than one life. Believe me, Lory, they mean what they say."

"But I can't back down now. What message would we be giving out if people knew I could be scared that easily?"

R.H. and Lory discussed the situation for the better part of an hour before coming up with a plan they thought would work. Since they both agreed that Lory had made her point with the public, there was no reason for her to remain in town. If there was a public-spirited citizen out there, he or she would be getting in touch with the police, and if not, Lory had done everything she could. Getting her safely away was a matter of keeping her protected until that could be accomplished.

R.H. had a friend with a private plane who agreed to take Lory wherever she wanted to go. They could leave as soon as it got light.

Lory put in her second phone call to Keith within twenty-four hours. She explained that she was free to rejoin the crew, and although she didn't like having to admit her vulnerability, it would be a good idea if she went somewhere remote for a few days. Unfortunately Keith was unable to accommodate her. The crew would be leaving for western Washington at daylight, too early for Lory to hook up with them. "By the way—" Keith continued "—would you please call Mike so he'll quit bothering me?"

"Mike," Lory breathed. There hadn't been time to think about him in the past few hours; his name brought everything back. "Why didn't you tell me yesterday?"

"Because he just started calling. You got a pen? I'll give you the number. You two figure it out. If you need to make yourself scarce, I'll bet he can think of something."

If Lory hadn't been used to Keith's blunt matchmaking, she would have blushed. Instead she wrote down the number Keith gave her and promised to rejoin the crew as soon as they returned from Washington. "It's crazy," she told R.H. after she'd hung up. "Sometimes I feel like a Ping-Pong ball bouncing all over the place."

"Where are you planning on going?" R.H. pressed. "Is it going to be safe?"

Of course she would be safe with Mike. Everything except her heart was safe when she was around him. Although it was late evening by now, Lory took a chance on dialing the number she'd been given. The older female voice that came on the line was that of Mike's mother.

Lory was talking to Mike's mother. "Thank heavens!" Nat Steen exclaimed. "That man's been driving me crazy. Just a minute. I'll get him."

The reaction Mike's mother had just described didn't fit the man Lory knew. Mike was calm, in control. He wouldn't run up a phone bill simply because he had an urge to talk to her. He'd wait—Lory wasn't sure what would prompt him to get in touch with her.

"Lory, are you all right?"

Lory stared at R.H., seeing not the powerfully built sheriff but the image of the man responsible for beautiful dreams and lonely nights. She remembered—a long kiss, shaky smiles, an emotion she'd never felt before, and not enough words at their parting. "Of course I'm all right. Why shouldn't I be?"

Mike breathed. She was alive. "I saw you on the news."

"Oh." Lory's voice faltered. He was concerned about her; it was in his voice. Taking a deep breath, she tried for a light tone. "What did you think? Did I get my point across?"

"Oh, you got your point across all right. You also put yourself on the firing line."

Lory wasn't angry. He might be taking exception to what she'd done, but it was so good to hear his voice that the subject didn't matter. "That was the only way we knew to make things work," she tried to explain. "Is that why you called Keith, because you didn't like what I said?"

"I called Keith because I didn't know how to get in touch with you."

Mike was being honest, too honest. She hadn't told him where she was going after their parting. But how could she? He hadn't told her where he'd be and she'd been too proud to ask. He hadn't told her what he was thinking; neither had she. What would he say if she said she'd fallen in love with him?

This was crazy! Why couldn't she say the words? "It worked," Lory admitted. "I got the message."

"I'm glad. Lory? I don't think it's safe to stay where you are."

Mike was thinking of her safety. True, the sheriff had done the same thing, but with Mike it was different. She'd given him her body, taken his. They'd shared so much and yet not enough. Now, maybe, there was a chance for more. Briefly Lory explained that she and R.H. had come to the same conclusion. "I'm going to be flying out of here in the morning," she explained.

"Where to?"

"I'm not sure. Probably home."

"Come here, Lory."

"You're serious?"

"Very. Will you?"

Would she? Mike, the man who had a hand over her heart, wanted to see her. "Yes."

At dawn, after a trip to the small airstrip in R.H.'s patrol car, Lory boarded a plane piloted by a local doctor and left northern Idaho behind. The doctor who attended to his widespread rural practice with the help of his own plane was happy to accommodate the sheriff, and to Lory's relief, kept up a steady conversation during the flight south. Asking just enough questions to keep the doctor's stories coming kept Lory's mind from what she was leaving. And what she was coming to.

Mike would be waiting at the Boise Air Terminal.

THIS TIME IT WAS she and not him who was climbing out of an aircraft. As Mike stood waiting, he wondered if she'd felt the same misgivings, the same eagerness when he'd arrived for their weekend on the Snake. He had needed more than a few days before he could understand what had happened to him that weekend. Not only had Mike felt part of a large, extended family but the member he'd found at its core had done things to his heart that had never been done before. They had needed space—he had needed space to think.

Or maybe he hadn't. The days had stretched in front of him like a lifeless desert. Knowing she was coming back to him had been the spring rain that brings the desert to life.

His official reason for inviting Lory here only scratched the surface. He'd made love to that woman, met her parents, joked with her brothers, heard about the most devastating experience in her life, held her in his arms and listened to her cry. That one incredible weekend bound them together.

Why the hell hadn't he told her that at the end of the weekend? Why had he let another goodbye be said?

"I don't know what I'm going to do with you," Mike said instead. Lory was out of the small plane, arms weighed down with a backpack and a small carryall. Her wind-blown hair drifted across her throat. Her dark eyes said he was the only person she wanted to see. Even with the pilot looking on, Mike didn't wait until he'd taken over her burdens before folding her in his arms. "Always bailing you out of scrapes.'' She was in his arms. Safe. And he was hope-lessly in love with her.

Lory looked surprised, as if she hadn't been ready for the embrace or the emotion behind his words. After an awkward moment, she introduced Mike to the pilot. "What are you doing at your mother's?" she asked.

"Being a dutiful son." Because his arms were now full, Mike couldn't hold Lory against him. Her arm brushed against his once as they headed toward his pickup. "Her car's falling apart. She seems to think that because I can keep a helicopter running, I should know something about cars."

Lory's laugh tore a swath through his resolve to take the day one slow step at a time. She was still smiling when they climbed into the truck. "I can't imagine your mother as a helpless female. Are you sure she isn't using this as an excuse to see you?"

"Could be. But since I like her cooking better than mine, I'm not going to complain too much about being conned. How's it been going? Any fires since last weekend?"

Lory gave him a thumbnail sketch of the boring days she'd spent wrestling with a report on the relative hardiness of Ponderosa versus Douglas firs before the arson case had come up. Mike tried to remember to nod, but found it impossible to concentrate. Lory was wearing some kind of cologne. Why then, he asked himself, hadn't she kissed him? Why was she sitting on her side of the truck?

"When are you going to make yourself available again?" Lory asked.

"I think I'm just about done with the repairs. But I'm not going to give myself a deadline, not now that you're here."

Don't say that, Mike. Being in the truck was tearing Lory apart. It shouldn't be so hard to make the decision to sit closer to him, but what if that wasn't what Mike wanted. "I won't be here long," she made herself say. She'd jammed her hands between her legs. It was the only way she could keep herself from reaching out and grabbing Mike with a strength that would give her away. "Keith doesn't think the crew will be in Washington long."

Mike was asking about Keith and Boyd and Ann, even about the small-town sheriff who'd insisted that Lory didn't belong in his county any longer. Lory didn't care about any of those things. She wanted to hear that Mike was as eager to have her meet his mother as she'd been to let him get to know her family.

But most of all, Lory wanted to know what Mike would say and think if she told him she loved him.

Mike skirted the center of Boise, taking her past the domed state capitol made of sandstone and Alaskan marble. From what she'd heard about the early years, Lory expected to find his mother living in primitive surroundings, but he pulled into a driveway in the middle of an older, carefully tended neighborhood, with the Owyhee Mountains providing a backdrop. Nat's white high-roofed house was on the small side, but the large yard was alive with greenery. In the open, freshly painted garage, Lory glimpsed a blue car with the hood up.

"I'm always teasing Mom about getting citified in her old age, but she maintains there's a lot to be said for a place that has garbage service, even if she did have to reroof it before she could move in. She's probably out in the garden."

"Garden?" Lory asked as she slid out of her side of the truck. "Are you serious?"

"Yep. She still likes people to believe she tills the soil, even though what she grows just keeps her and a few neighbors supplied." Mike had left Lory's belongings in the truck, which left his arms free. Before they'd reached the house, he used his freedom to take Lory into his arms. Her head was uplifted when his lips came down on hers. Their kiss lasted much longer than necessary for a simple hello.

"You smell fantastic," he whispered.

"Thank you," Lory whispered back without explaining.

"Like roses. I didn't know you wore cologne."

"I don't usually." Lory didn't break eye contact. "I felt like it today."

"Lory?" Mike had started to guide Lory around to the backyard, but now stopped her. "I missed you."

"I needed to hear that."

Mike's mother was a woman framed by a lifetime of independence. Although in her late fifties, she carried herself with the ease of someone much younger. She was of average height and weight but before Lory had spent more than a couple of minutes with her, she'd sensed the strength flowing through the woman. Nat's handshake was firm and decisive; her eye contact demanded honesty.

Nat explained that she'd taken the day off work to spend with her son, but if he was going to shirk his mechanical responsibilities, she wasn't going to waste her own time. "There's one thing I've learned about this son of mine," Nat explained. "He's going to do what he wants, when he wants. I have no idea how he grew up so cussed independent."

Lory tried to laugh off Nat's comment, but her laugh came out weaker than she wanted it to. Mike did what he wanted, when he wanted, even where his mother was concerned. Could she expect it to be any different for her?

Without needing much convincing, Nat agreed to drop her gardening and join Lory and Mike on the rear patio. Over iced tea, Lory learned that Mike had been open with his mother about his reasons for asking Lory to come here.

"I work with kids who have had their share of scrapes with the law," Nat explained. "Believe me, I know about people who don't have any conscience. I'd probably jump on the first plane out of town myself."

Lory had been thinking about the contrast between where she'd begun her day and Nat Steen's fenced backyard. Watching a trio of small birds fighting over bugs in the garden was a lifetime away from the never-ending job of protecting the nation's forests. It seemed incredible that a woman who knew all there was to know about the growing of asparagus was equally knowledgeable about the darker side of human nature. "What kind of students do you have?" Lory asked.

Nat explained that for the past few years she'd been working at a vocational high school teaching potential dropouts. "It's a pilot program," she explained. "What we're trying to do is give these teens a taste of the real world, hopefully so they'll stay in school and complete their educations. It's a hard sell, but I have no qualms about letting them talk to people with criminal records, welfare recipients. Most of those who aren't making it in today's world are those who don't have an education."

Spurred on by the encouragement in Mike's eyes, Lory expressed her approval of what Nat was doing. Lory explained that the forest service hired a number of young people for fire fighting and other summer activities, but advancement for anyone without a high-school education was next to impossible. "I worry that we're giving some kids a false message," she wound up. "They earn good money doing a dangerous job, but we can't offer them any job security."

Lory caught the look passing between Mike and his mother. "Don't even think it, Mom," Mike warned while covering Lory's arm with a protective hand. "Lory's here for a vacation."

"Vacation, nothing," Nat snorted. "How would you like to talk to my kids? You'll be here tomorrow, won't you?"

Lory wanted to concentrate on what she was being asked, but Mike was touching her. He hadn't done that since their too-quick kiss and hastily spoken words at the front door. She heard herself agreeing to Nat's proposal. "I remember what I was like at that age," Lory admitted. "I wasn't much interested in the wisdom of my elders. I don't know how much they'll want to hear."

"Just be honest with them. Tell them what you like and don't like about your job. Let them know what kind of schooling and training you had to have in order to get where you are."

"Where she is, Mom," Mike said pointedly, "is relaxing. Or she would be if you didn't wear your teacher hat twenty-four hours a day."

"What do you know? I know I should have knocked you around more while you were growing up. Darn whipper-snapper thinks he knows it all."

"I do know it all," Mike shot back while Lory laughed. "After all, look at the role model I had."

"Do something with him," Nat begged. "I've never been able to keep him in line. He needs a woman who won't take any nonsense from him."

"I couldn't agree more," Lory said, laughing. As quickly as that mood had overtaken her, it was replaced by a more sober one. "However, I don't see enough of Mike to have any influence over him."

Mike was quiet for so much of the day that Lory was left to worry about the wisdom of her words. Although she tried to busy herself by handing Mike tools while he worked on his mother's car, she was acutely aware of the quiet way he watched her. Lory would have felt more comfortable if Nat had been with them, but she'd insisted that if Mike was going to tinker with her car, she might as well borrow his truck to run errands. Being alone with Mike, on his turf, was not what Lory's nerves needed.

Mike represented something she'd never experienced before.

By the time Mike had his mother's car engine back together, dinner was ready. After washing up, Lory helped Nat
carry the large chef's salad and bakery bread onto the patio. Nat handed Lory a glass of wine without waiting for
Mike to join them. "I didn't mean for it to sound as if I'm
pushing you," Nat said as she sat in the lawn chair next to
Lory's. "If you don't want to come to school tomorrow, tell
me."

"Oh, no," Lory assured her. "I'm looking forward to it.
I'm warning you though, if I get going on what I like about
my job, you might have to drag me out of there."

"You really do like what you do?"

"Yes, I do." Lory took a sip of wine and concentrated on
Mike's mother. "I think that's one of the positive things
about not having anyone dependent on me. I can do what I
want. I don't have to stick with a job simply because it pro-
vides an income."

"Amen!" Nat patted Lory on the shoulder before concentrating on her glass. "I've seen so many people get
locked into jobs they hate. I can't imagine what that must
be like. I think I was born to be a teacher. Imparting
knowledge, to say nothing of having a captive audience, is
a real turn-on."

Lory laughed. "I like your honesty."

"It takes honesty and a lot more to do what I've done,"
Nat said softly. "I take it Mike told you about his father.
Neither of us has heard from him since Mike was five or six.
There were a lot of benefits to being a single parent, Lory. I
didn't have to ask a husband's opinion or take a husband's
feelings into consideration. As long as I made enough to
keep food on the table, I could do whatever I wanted to.
Fortunately I found a career that coincided with my son's
needs."

Lory didn't have to weigh the consequences of telling Nat
what was on her mind. In the short amount of time she'd

known Mike's mother, she'd come to understand what the older woman meant about honesty. "You did a good job with him. You raised a very independent man."

"Too damn independent."

"What?"

"I'm sure you've seen it," Nat explained. "I'm the only person Mike has had to feel responsible for. If it wasn't for checking in with me every once in a while, who knows where he'd wander off to. And—it isn't just that." After a pause, Nat went on. "I don't know if it's a result of his upbringing, or if Mike has some of his father in him, but it's been hard for him to develop relationships. He's self-contained, if you know what I mean."

"I think I do." Whenever Lory thought of Mike, there was the image of a man free of the constraints of earth. No one except a mother to share his life with. No ties to any place except a house Lory had never seen.

"Mike's self-reliant, which is a good thing up to a point. I think he's happy. I hope he is. But sometimes, well, I'm a typical mother. I want my son to have someone. I wish you could see his place. That's all I can call it—a place. I've worked my fingers to the bone fixing up my home, but Mike hasn't done anything with his and it needs work. I'd never tell him, but I think that's because it's only a place to hang his hat."

"Oh," Lory whispered. On the Snake, her own mother had been able to tell Mike about her fears and dreams for her daughter. Now Mike's mother was doing the same thing.

"I'm not trying to push my son at you." Nat laughed, but the sound came out forced. "But, Lory, you share a lot of things with Mike."

"I do?"

"Both of you are rootless. I hope I haven't offended you, but I know the condition. I saw it in my husband, and now my son." Nat sighed. "There are other similarities. Neither of you would be doing what you're doing if you didn't feel commitment to something that goes a lot deeper than money. And, Lory, I think both of you are looking for someone to share life with.''

Chapter Eleven

Earlier Mike had taken Lory's belongings into the spare bedroom he used when visiting his mother. Now Lory stood at the entrance staring at the double bed, wondering whether Mike would be sleeping on the couch or in here with her. With the long hours stretching back beyond dawn dragging at her, Lory slipped out of her jeans and blouse without giving the act much thought. She turned at the sound of Mike entering the room.

Say something, she thought, but Mike only stared at her for a long minute before turning off the overhead light. His bare feet made no sound as he crossed the room. Wordlessly he took her into his arms.

"You don't have to do this if you don't want to," he whispered after a kiss that spirited Lory out of the bedroom and back to the banks of the Snake River. He swallowed and the words came slowly. "I don't have any claim on you."

Don't say that, Lory silently begged. *You have a claim on my heart.* "Mike? Why did you invite me here?" she pressed.

"I told you." Caught against his chest, Mike's voice reached her as a soft reverberation. "I was worried about you."

"Is that the only reason?"

"No," Mike answered, but whatever other reasons he had were expressed in action and not words. Gently he lifted her in his arms and carried her to the bed. Mike sat on the edge, his hands soft on Lory's shoulders. "I thought about this when we were on the Snake. Not being at my mother's house, but making love to you in a real bed."

"The ground was hard there," Lory managed to say. Although she was wearing nothing but underwear, Mike's hands were chaste. It was, she thought, as if he knew he had all the time in the world to explore her.

"I didn't mind." Mike's lips left their imprint on her chin, her eyelids, her right ear. With each kiss, Lory lost a little of herself and gained something precious. "The first time was special, Lory."

The first time. *How many more times will there be, Mike?* She'd tried to keep her hands limp at her sides, but they needed him too much. Smiling a little, Lory spread her fingers over his shoulders and drew him down to her. In the few weeks that Mike had been part of her life, Lory had come to accept certain things. Each time might be the last. She had no claims on him, would make no demands. He'd chosen to share this night with her. That was as far as she would allow her heart to travel.

Mike was warmth, a pulsing heat for her body to absorb like a hungry sponge. She'd started to lose herself the moment he'd walked into the room. Now the loss became so great that she no longer knew which one of them she heard breathing.

Not that breathing mattered. She had to listen. "I asked you something earlier," he was whispering. "Do you want this?"

Rising upward until she had found his mouth, Lory gave her answer in action. This was no virgin kiss. Everything she thought she'd understood about their relationship evaporated, leaving her with nothing except wanting him. There could be no question; he had to know how much tonight meant.

Mike's hands were everywhere now. Beginning at her throat, they slid to her shoulders and ran slowly down her arms. He removed her bra so smoothly that Lory was barely aware of her nakedness until his lips came down to claim her breasts. Lory arched her spine in response, reaching for him, needing everything he was willing to give.

Were they really separate beings? The question surfaced but died under the impact of much more powerful emotions. Lory was molten energy in Mike's hands. Like a wild bird in the grip of a gentle master, she accepted the warm strength surrounding her. But unlike a captive bird, Lory couldn't remain quiet. She needed what he was and could become for her more than she'd needed anything in life. If it took strong fingers and hungry lips to satisfy that need, so be it.

Mike left her long enough to remove his own clothes. When he returned to her, he pulled off her underpants with a quick, impatient gesture. "You're beautiful, Lory. So beautiful," he said before claiming her mouth again. "You're so easy to love."

Love. What a magic, powerful word. But because Lory believed that, for Mike, the word was a puff of smoke in an uncertain wind, Lory fought her heart's wild, unwise beating. "You're easy to love, too, Mike."

Love! She'd said the word. Did he dare believe she felt what he felt? Don't do it, Mike warned himself. Don't ask for too much.

She was his; he was hers. For tonight.

In the wild lovemaking that followed, Lory learned a fundamental lesson about the art of giving and taking. Giving meant surrendering what had always been at the core of her being and sharing it with another human being. Taking meant accepting the offered gifts and safeguarding what he was willing to share. The competent loner was no more. For the few minutes that they were one, Lory held in her hands more than Mike had ever given another human being. He was man and child, master and slave. She by turn gave full rein to the passionate creature so long buried within her.

Their first lovemaking was an explosion of giving and taking, saying nothing and doing everything. In this quick, hungry coming together there was little time for lingering exploration. That came later.

After resting with their heated bodies entwined, they reached out again. This time there was time for foreplay. Lory committed Mike's body to memory. He did the same for her. It seemed to Lory that the exploration took hours and yet every second was the only one that existed. Whenever her desires threatened to crest, Mike instinctively knew what to do to allow her to ride out the tide. By turn she too learned something essential and precious about drawing out her man's pleasure. He'd placed himself in her hands; in gratitude for his gift, she treated him with reverence and love. When, finally, the ultimate act of trust came again, Lory held on to her emotions and feelings, savoring their lovemaking instead of charging through it. She was standing at a cliff, arms outstretched, and yet the plunge could wait until she was certain they were going over it together.

Hours later as dawn kissed the room, they woke and repeated the loving act. Lory lay satiated as Mike slipped out of bed and opened the window. He drew in fresh morning air. "I've never spent a night like that. Never known it was possible."

"You haven't?" Last night, with Mike, had been perfection so exquisite that a mountain spring was pale by comparison. She needed to know he felt the same.

"I didn't know. I didn't know it could be that good." A look of amazement touched his features. "Lory? You touched me in ways I didn't know possible."

Lory had never thought of herself as the kind of woman a man would turn to for a night of abandon, but that was before Mike had pushed the right buttons, opened the right door. If she'd been in any way responsible for taking Mike places he'd never been before, it was only because he was the right one for her. Even now his naked body held her attention. If it wasn't for her promise to his mother, Lory would have held out her arms and drawn Mike back to her.

It wasn't just lovemaking she wanted. If Mike had exhausted himself, she would be content to simply fall asleep in his arms. That was the truly wonderful thing about the night. They'd spent hours simply holding each other, sharing emotions and feelings that didn't need words or action. And if there were words, a word, wrapped inside that hadn't been said—maybe tomorrow.

Lory winced as the alarm went off in Nat's room. Mike started toward the bathroom but then turned back toward her. He leaned over her, his magnificent naked body both familiar and exciting. "I won't be long," he whispered with his lips on hers. "Thank you."

"Thank you?"

"For last night."

"Thank you, too." The words came from Lory's heart.

After a shower that Lory barely remembered, she dressed in a soft short-sleeved sweater and cream slacks before joining Mike and his mother in the kitchen. Winking, Mike handed her a cup of coffee. "I remembered," he told her. "I'm not to expect anything intelligent out of you until you've had your caffeine."

It had taken makeup for Lory to erase the evidence of her night, but Mike seemed to have returned to sanity without any such aid. Lory wasn't sure how she felt about that. She wanted to see something, anything, in his eyes to remind her of the three times they'd entrusted their separate selves to each other. Without doing more than fixing his hazel eyes on hers, Mike turned to teasing his mother about asking Lory to address her class because she was too lazy to have prepared a lesson plan. Nat responded spiritedly to her son's kidding; there was nothing in her demeanor to indicate she'd heard anything last night.

After coffee and cereal, the trio climbed into Nat's car and left for school. Because Mike and his mother were interested in how the car handled, Lory remained quiet. She tried to focus on her surroundings, but her thoughts kept turning to how comfortable she felt sandwiched between Mike and his mother. They'd been a unit for years, best friends who'd transcended the mother/son relationship. And yet, at least for today, they were giving her a place within that unit. She could do nothing less than love them for that.

Lory had no preconceptions about what Nat's class was like, so a roomful of boys in faded jeans and wrinkled T-shirts with a few equally casually dressed girls sprinkled through it didn't faze her. Lory had seen enough young summer forest-service employees that she could recognize teens who wanted nothing more out of life than money in their pockets. Lory and Mike sat quietly in the back of the room until Nat had finished with the morning routine. Then Mike's mother made her introduction.

"I know you were all looking forward to that film on a day in the life of a policeman, but we'll just have to hold off on the popcorn until tomorrow. I've been able to bribe a young woman into talking to you characters. Lory Foster has the kind of job they should make a movie out of. Lory, it's all yours."

Lory walked to the front of the room and faced the wary eyes. Nat had joined Mike at the back of the room, but she didn't let herself be distracted by his presence. She'd tried to describe her job to others in the past, but the focus today would have to be different. Lory began by telling the students about the first time she'd parachuted out of an airplane. "I was scared to death up until the moment I was out of the plane. Then I felt as if I'd somehow conquered gravity. I was weightless, the wind was tugging at my face, and it was all I could do to remember what I was there for. I wasn't doing it for the thrill," she finished up. "It was part of my job. Have I given any of you a clue?"

The first guesses were off the mark, but a lanky boy at the back of the room had the correct answer. "You're a smoke jumper, aren't you? My brother used to do that before he went into the army," he explained. "He didn't work all the time, so it wasn't that hot a job."

"Your brother was right about that," Lory agreed. "Fortunately, I'm a full-time employee of the forest service, so I always have a paycheck coming in. I didn't give fire fighting much thought when I first went to work for the service, but there was some training scheduled and when I heard what I'd earn while fighting fires I decided to give it a shot. I've been hooked ever since."

"How come?" a girl asked. "It's awfully hard work, isn't it?"

"Yes, it's hard. And it's dangerous," Lory admitted. "But there are compensations that make it worthwhile." At the girl's blank look, Lory gave it another shot. "Look, you know how important your friends are. Sharing, having common interests, knowing your friends will back you up no matter what you do, that's what really matters, isn't it? Well, it's like that but even more so with the members of a team. There are times when we rely on each other for our lives. That results in a bond that goes so deep I can't explain it. All I know is, I'd be lost without that bond." Lory caught Mike's gaze, read something somber in his eyes, then struggled to go on.

"It's...it's important to me to feel I'm doing something essential with my life. Fighting a fire, saving wildlife, protecting someone's home, those are things I can look to with a sense of pride. I also enjoy a physical challenge. One of my brothers says I like to live life on the edge. Maybe he's right.''

Lory had hoped that the class would be interested in the nuts and bolts of how to get into forestry, but she wasn't surprised when the questions focused around what they considered the exciting aspects of fighting fires. She gave them a rundown on how she lived during the fire season, what it was like to actually fight a fire, how computers and other modern advancements were being used to predict the course and nature of a fire, some of the more spectacular burns she'd been involved in. She didn't want to glamorize what she did; neither did she want to downplay its importance. Although she talked for the better part of an hour, Mike's eyes didn't leave her. He was there, feeling what she was saying, taking in what she was giving out. Sharing.

Finally she was asked the question she'd been waiting for. One boy who'd remained quiet up until now asked how she felt when she looked at a forest that had been burned. ''Do you want an honest answer?'' she asked. She pressed a hand to her stomach. ''It makes me sick. Does that sound strange? I've just told you what a turn-on fighting fires can be and now I'm saying I hate the results. But it does make me sick to see a vital, living forest turned into ashes and blackened stumps. It makes me damn mad, especially if the fire was caused by carelessness or a deliberate act of arson.'' Lory glanced at Nat to see if she was shocked by her use of profanity but was distracted by Mike's slowly nodding head. If no one else in the room did, at least Mike understood.

Lory wasn't content to leave her reply at that. She went on to explain that, although fires were devastating both in terms of lost timber and money, man could now do a lot to rectify the damage. She highlighted the role of the forest service in the replanting of burned acreage. Replacing downed trees began soon after a fire was out. Even before the trees grew to any size, the forest ground came alive with ferns, grasses and other ground cover.

"There's something else I'd like all of you to understand," Lory finished up. "Not all fires are bad. In fact, if we know that a fire is going to remain contained and won't threaten any commercial timber, we let it burn itself out. Fire is a natural process. It keeps plant species in control. It's only when fires are out of control that we pull out all the stops. In fact, that's how I met your teacher's son. We were both fighting a fire. Mike? Is there anything you'd like to add?"

It was obvious that this wasn't the first time Mike had addressed the students. They knew him by name and most of them had seen his helicopter. Still, they kept Mike busy answering questions for the rest of the period. Lory was waiting for Mike to join her when the lanky boy who'd asked the first question came up to her. "Can I ask you something, Miss Foster?"

"Anything."

"What you've been saying makes a lot of sense. I mean, I don't know what I want to do with my life. Maybe I should look into what you're doing, but I still don't get it."

Lory had told the boy he could ask her anything. She wasn't going to back out now. "What don't you get?"

"Why do you do it? I mean, I can see some big guy like Mike risking his neck, but you're, well, you're not very big. Doesn't it scare you? Wouldn't you rather be doing something safe?"

"I think about that sometimes," Lory admitted as Mike joined her. "Yes, there are times when I'm scared. Not often, but it happens. I've—I lost someone special in a fire. But a certain amount of danger keeps me from getting bored." Lory laughed at herself. "I'm like a little kid. I need something happening all the time. I want to do something important with my life. I don't want to spend it working at a car wash or making hamburgers.''

Mike kept his hand on Lory's shoulder, but he was unaware of her searching glance. The past hour had been an incredible experience for him. He'd been convinced of Lory's competence before, but watching her conduct herself in front of a roomful of strangers further reinforced that impression.

But it went beyond admiration. This morning he'd been the student. He'd learned things he hadn't known about how sophisticated computers tracked the patterns of a fire. Surely it hadn't been necessary for her to know about sensors, satellites, solar-powered weather stations, automated lightning detectors. She knew those things because she had an insatiable curiosity about her world.

Curiosity was only half of the story. Even though Lory had confessed to moments of fear, it was clear that she was in control of the wild, unpredictable world she'd chosen to live in. A woman who accepted that a down-flowing wind through the mountain ranges could result in surface wind speeds of sixty miles an hour had to be self-contained.

Maybe a woman like that didn't need a man like him. What did he mean, maybe? Look what she'd done with her life before he'd entered—tried to enter it.

''That was quite an experience,'' Lory was saying after Mike's mother had taken them into the teachers' lounge. ''I can see why people become teachers. It's quite a charge to have a roomful of people hanging on your every word.''

''That doesn't happen very often,'' Nat admitted. ''Most of the time I'm lucky if I can keep them awake. I'm going to have to give some thought to wearing a hard hat, with a shovel over my shoulder.''

Trying to ignore Mike's unsettling silence, Lory focused on Nat. Until the bell announcing the next class rang, she pumped Nat for details on what her long-range goals for her students were. Finally, though, only Mike and Lory were left in the lounge. Mike was methodically poking holes through an empty Styrofoam container. "When do you have to leave?" he asked.

Hurt, Lory explained that she had been thinking about getting in touch with the Interagency Fire Center to see when her crew would be returning. "I'd also like to call my sheriff friend to see if anything's come of that arson case. Mike? Did I tell you thank you?"

Mike released the shredded white remains to cover Lory's hand with cool fingers. "For what?"

For last night. For making me believe, for a few minutes at least, that you needed me. "For giving me a place to hide out. It's hard to think of myself as being in protective custody, but I guess that's what it was. R.H. said that whoever was doing that illegal logging didn't think twice about setting fires, so why should I think they would stop at murder?"

"Murder." Mike drew out the word. "It's a hell of a way to earn a living, isn't it?"

"What?" Why was Mike doing this? She was already so insecure around him. "Are you talking about the illegal loggers?"

"I'm talking about you, Lory. I think your mother is right to worry."

"Don't start on that, please," Lory warned. "I've loved being here. I don't want anything to spoil it."

"In other words, don't say what's on my mind."

Lory sank back in the plastic chair. *Don't leave me, Mike. Not after what we had.* "No," she said, forcing out the words. "That's not what I mean. All right, what's on your mind?"

"I think . . . I think I don't like your job."

"What?"

"Jeff died, Lory. The same could happen to you."

Lory had had all she could handle. She could take Mike's silence, even the transient nature of their relationship— words of love that didn't go beyond the bedroom. What she didn't want or need was an attack on her profession. "What about you, Mike?" she countered. "How would you feel if I told you I don't want you flying Igor anymore?" She'd been staring at nothing; now she turned on Mike. "You could be killed."

"You're right." Mike got to his feet. "I could. We both could. Come on, you've got some phone calls to make."

Lory fought to concentrate on the tasks in front of her, but Mike's silence was an unrelenting pressure. He'd been everything she could want in a lover and friend last night. She'd believed, honestly believed, that they might have more than last night. She hated the changes that had taken place since then. She hated their having spoken this truth.

There was a message on Mike's mother's answering machine asking Mike to call the fire center. His services were needed east of Spokane near the Washington/Idaho border. The sooner he could get to Coeur d'Alene the better. It's ending again, Lory forced herself to admit. Another goodbye would have to be said.

Because Keith and the crew weren't expected to be done for another two days, Lory thought she might be the one left behind, but that was before she called R.H. The sheriff told her he'd been in contact with a college student who'd been hiking, illegally, through forest-service land when it had been torched. The student hadn't said anything for fear of getting into trouble himself, but that was before Lory had gone public with the promise of a reward. Now that the student had been offered immunity, he was willing to identify the men who'd set the fire. However, in order to build a solid case, the district attorney was calling for Lory's testimony to back up the contention that the fire had been deliberate. The sooner Lory could turn in her statement, the sooner the men could be charged.

"He's expecting me," Lory moaned. "I wish—"

"What?"

"Nothing." She'd almost said she wished she had more time here, but Mike's silence after leaving the school had been her warning. She wasn't going to expose any more of herself than he had. "I think I'd better leave now. Will you tell your mother I appreciated her hospitality?"

Let her go, Mike told himself. He'd never needed anyone before. What did he know about this thing called love? But if she walked out the door now, he might never recapture the magic they'd shared last night. Step beyond the hard, honest words that had been said in the teachers' lounge, he told himself. "You tell her, tonight," he heard himself saying. "Stay until dinner, Lory. I'll fly you back."

Lory had been given a few more hours with Mike. She wanted to throw her arms around him, cry out her thankfulness. Instead she heard herself calmly, coolly agreeing and then pointing out that tonight she wanted to prepare the meal.

Lory and Mike filled the day with shopping and sightseeing. Buying what they'd need for a chef's salad and marinated steaks didn't take nearly long enough. As soon as the purchases had been deposited in the refrigerator, Mike had them back in his mother's car again. Until it was time to pick Nat up, they crisscrossed the city known as the City of Trees. Mike pointed out Table Rock, which had once served as an Indian lookout, the Old Idaho penitentiary, the ten-mile bicycle and pedestrian path that followed the Boise River. Although Lory had been to Boise before, she'd seldom been anywhere but the Interagency Fire Center and the state capitol. With Mike serving as guide, Lory was able to find the flow between past and present.

Nat was collecting test papers when Mike and Lory came by the school to pick her up. "You two ruined things for me today," she declared. "Those characters were so revved up I couldn't do a thing with them. The boys were all going to be helicopter pilots before you came along, Lory. Now they don't know whether they're going to follow in my son's footsteps or aim for the fame and glory of fire fighting. A couple of them talk as if they're ready to make their living as smoke jumpers. It hasn't occurred to them that they have no idea what they'll do once they hit the ground."

For the first time in hours, Lory relaxed enough to smile. She was grateful for Nat's presence, both in the car and then in the kitchen while she went about preparing dinner. Mike had gone out to the garage to adjust the timing on his mother's car, which gave Lory some breathing room. "I'm going to have to go back to Wallace tonight," Lory explained. "I don't think I should have told Mike that I'd been threatened. It's causing a problem."

"That man!" Nat waited until Lory peeled a hard-boiled egg and snagged a slice for herself. "Stand firm, Lory. Don't let him try to make your decisions for you. What am I talking about? You're one woman who will never let that happen. Besides—" Nat grew wistful "—my son isn't the kind of man to see himself as a white knight for all womankind. I showed him that I can stand on my own two feet. Now he thinks every woman can do the same thing."

"That's good, isn't it?" Lory asked.

"Up to a point. But aren't there times when you could go for a little pampering?"

"Sometimes," Lory admitted. "But the urge passes. Nat, Mike and I are pretty independent people." Too independent.

"So I've noticed. Sometimes it's good and sometimes a large dose of competence can backfire. A little needing never hurt anyone. I'm going to tell you something I haven't told many people. My husband—I was as responsible for our problems as he was. I wasn't content to sit at home waiting for my man to return. I built my own life. Frank couldn't handle that.'' Nat gave Lory a compassionate squeeze. ''Learn from my mistakes if you can, Lory. Don't block other people out.''

I'm not, Lory tried to tell herself. Mike's the one who's blocking me out. But it was more complicated than that. Too complicated for her heart to deal with.

By unspoken agreement, Mike and Lory kept the conversation general during dinner. There had been more opportunity to talk once they were in the air, but Lory had let the minutes and then the hours slip away without saying anything. Mike had made her believe he wanted something to change between them when he invited her to Boise, but the feeling hadn't lasted any longer than their lovemaking. Something had closed around him this morning, something Lory would have slashed away at if Mike had only given her a clue as to what she was fighting.

But he wasn't saying anything. Instead he was landing near the doctor's small plane and was putting an end to their flight. The helicopter rocked forward and then settled back. Lory braced herself, not because she expected to be thrown from her seat, but because there was nothing left to hold them together.

''I guess that's it,'' Lory whispered once her belongings were on the ground. ''Are you sure you can't stay, Mike?'' Lory shied from her question, but the shock didn't last long. She'd only said what was in her heart.

Stay, Mike told himself. She wants it. You want it. But if they spent the night together, he might give more of himself than she was willing to give. Lory didn't need him. She was much too competent for that. Somehow he would return to what he was before she entered his life. ''I need to spend the night in Coeur d'Alene. That way I can get to the fire as soon as it gets light."

Of course. Mike had a job. He would always have a job that meant more to him than any woman. Lory tried to hold out her hand for a handshake, but somehow her hand wound up around Mike's neck. He didn't resist when she pulled him down for a kiss.

It was a mistake. Lory should have known better than to allow herself back into Mike's arms. They had the night-darkened airstrip to themselves. If she wasn't careful, Lory might lose whatever control she had over her emotions. It would be so easy to give him everything. Her heart was tired of saying goodbye, of never knowing when—or if—she'd see Mike again.

I need you, Mike. For tonight and tomorrow and the rest of my life.

"Tell your mother hello for me," she said instead. "I'm glad I was able to meet her."

"She likes you. And you made a hit with her kids." Damn! That wasn't what he wanted to say at all! Lory was still in his arms, her slight frame making a lie of what he believed she was. A woman who could give herself completely to a night of lovemaking should want more than that one night. But she hadn't said anything about wanting more. And Mike had his pride.

Maybe losing Jeff had done something irreparable to Lory. Was that what he'd seen in his mother's classroom this morning? Not the easy competence of a woman in touch with what she needed out of life, but a woman wary of making another commitment. Mike believed that Jeff and Lory had been friends and not lovers, but Lory had given Jeff a great deal.

Maybe there wasn't anything left for her to give.

The sound of an approaching engine pulled Mike and Lory apart. Lory stood looking up at Mike, hurting because she couldn't see enough of him in the dark. She wasn't going to cry, wasn't going to say anything. Mike was eager to get back into his helicopter and rejoin the world he knew so well. He didn't need her. Mike didn't need any woman.

She could take saying goodbye again; she had no choice.

"We do a lot of this, don't we?" Mike asked in a whisper.

"Yes, we do."

"I've been thinking about that." Mike swallowed, waiting for his thoughts to come together. "I don't know any way around it. Lory, my job's unpredictable. Yours isn't any different. I don't think either of us is ready for any commitments right now." *Liar!*

"I agree. I'm—glad we're able to admit that." *Liar.*

"Be careful." Mike's hands slid down Lory's arms, paused at her fingers and then dropped away.

Say something! Tell me you hate this as much as I do! "I can take care of myself, Mike."

Chapter Twelve

Lory watched the newcomer with a critical eye. She'd been around fire fighters long enough that she'd developed a sixth sense about them. This time her sense was telling her that the twenty-two-year-old had too much enthusiasm and not enough wisdom under his belt.

Ann shared her opinion. "I don't know what the big deal is with Sal's pregnancy. She's not the first woman to have high blood pressure, for crying out loud," the older fire fighter complained.

"It's more than that," Lory pointed out. "I don't blame Boyd. If it was my wife, I'd be there, not here." Five minutes after hearing from Keith that Boyd wouldn't be with them this time, Lory had been on the phone. Talking to Boyd had settled her fear that Sal might be in danger of losing the baby. Still, she understood Boyd's belief that he was the only one who could make Sal take it easy until the baby was born. Lory had talked to Sal for a few minutes and then hung up after making Boyd and Sal promise to call her the moment the baby was born.

Ann was still complaining. "I'm comfortable around Boyd. I don't want that punk kid coming in taking his place. Especially not where we're heading today."

Lory was inclined to agree with Ann. In a matter of minutes they'd be climbing into a fat-bellied old plane that would take them to the Payette National Forest, where they'd parachute into the old-growth timber that was in the path of an out-of-control wall of fire. Aaron Phillips might be competent, but Lory would rather have him prove that during a mop-up operation and not in the middle of an incinerator. "I hate parachuting into these things," Lory admitted. "Especially with what the wind's doing."

"Just think of the overtime," Ann pointed out. "I know I need it. That dumb husband of mine went and bought himself a new truck. Can you believe that! I didn't know a thing until I called him the other day. Why do I put up with him?" For a moment, a softening Lory had never seen transformed Ann's face. "Because he puts up with me. Lordy, I love that man!" Ann shook her big hands as if trying to shake off water. "I want to get out of here! When are we going to get going?"

"Calm down," Lory admonished, although she was feeling the same tension, the same need to be on the move. At least Mike hadn't taken that from her. "You're going to scare Aaron."

Ann looked over to where the young man was digging his toe into the earth. "I don't trust him. Too young. Too green."

"Hey," Lory said, laughing. "We were young and green ourselves once."

"I was never young. I think I was born old. Either that or that husband of mine has been giving me gray hairs for so long that I can't remember when it started. So how was it? Keith told us about that arson business. He also said something about a side trip to see what's his name. Why aren't you still with him?"

"Because someone has to keep you on track." To emphasize her point, Lory made an unnecessary check of the fastenings on Ann's backpack. She could hear the engine on the plane that would carry them into the wilderness kick into life.

"Sorry, old girl, but I don't buy that. This is the first time I've ever seen you give a guy more than a nod. We were all taking bets on whether this was the one. You don't want me to lose a perfectly good five dollars, do you?"

Lory shook her head. At least bantering with Ann gave her something to think about. "And what direction was your bet going?"

"That you were finally going to tie the knot."

"Then you're out five dollars, Ann. There isn't any knot to tie."

"Why not?" Ann asked. Although the plane had started to taxi closer, neither woman moved.

"I don't know. Or maybe I do and I just don't want to admit it," Lory replied honestly. "It felt right when I was around him. But he's a loner. He doesn't need anyone."

"Bull!"

"Believe me," Lory said. "I know what I'm talking about. Look, I'm not going to chase after some man who doesn't need more out of life than some helicopter named Igor. I have my pride."

"Pride be damned." Ann picked up her duffel bag and hefted it to her shoulder. "Look, don't you ever blab to that turkey I'm married to, but the first time I saw him, I knew he was the one for me. I chased that hunk until he caught me."

Lory could laugh at that. A moment later she sobered. That wasn't happening with her and Mike. He didn't want to be caught, and she wasn't going to chase. "Both of you wanted to be caught," she pointed out. "Mike doesn't."

"How do you know? Have you asked him?"

Sighing, Lory fell in line behind Ann as the older woman started toward the waiting plane. "Not with words. But I have."

Although she was ready to climb into the plane, Ann turned back toward Lory. "If you feel you can't ask him, it's because the answer matters too much. How do you think I felt? I was scared to death that turkey of mine was going to get away. Let me ask you something. Have you let him know how you feel?"

The question stopped Lory. She'd invited Mike to spend a weekend with her family. She'd told him about Jeff. She'd gone to him when he asked her to. Told him—sort of—that she loved him. Those gestures should have been message enough. "Not in words," she repeated. "But—"

"But nothing." Frowning, Ann stepped back to let Aaron squeeze in ahead of her. "Look, men can be pretty dense sometimes." She gave Aaron's back a telling stare. "Women have to hit them over the head if they're ever going to get the point."

"But, Ann, what if he doesn't feel the way I do?"

"How do you feel?"

This conversation was getting her nowhere. Lory was no closer to understanding either herself or Mike than she'd been after she'd agreed that too much was keeping them apart, that they should accept those forces. "I don't know."

Grunting, Ann hoisted herself into the plane's belly. She grabbed the bags Lory tossed her and leaned out to give Lory a hand. "I think you know what you feel all right. You just don't know how to spit it out."

Ann meant well, but that wasn't it at all. Mike had his job. His life. Maybe she meant something to him when they were together, but the feeling wasn't strong enough.

Let it go, Lory whispered for the hundredth time since she'd last seen Mike. This morning she was on her way to try to stop a raging inferno. Mike belonged to yesterday.

By the time the smoke jumpers settled into the plane, it was time to take off. Conversation centered around where they were headed and what they knew about the fire raging out of control at the edge of a magnificent stand of old-growth timber. Conservation groups were calling for an all-out assault to stop the fire before it destroyed the virgin timber. According to those groups, certain species of wildlife, particularly the northern spotted owl, needed old-growth timber in order to survive. Lory's own research indicated that the situation might not be that extreme, but even if a species wasn't in jeopardy, it was essential that this fire be contained.

Most of the crew, although eager to begin work, had learned the art of patience. Aaron was another story. The young man was practically bouncing off the walls in his eagerness to reach his first real fire. Along with giving Ann telling looks, Lory occupied herself by helping Aaron run over what he'd been taught about fire-fighting techniques. By the time they were in sight of the fire, Lory was convinced that Aaron understood his job; she just wasn't sure he would be coolheaded enough to remember what he'd been taught.

"This is fantastic!" Aaron gushed as the plane's pilot circled above the small meadow the smoke jumpers were about to parachute into. "Wait till I tell my girlfriend. She thinks my job's fantastic!"

Lory groaned. Any more enthusiasm from Aaron and she'd be tempted to shove her hard hat into his mouth to keep him quiet. She risked a long-suffering glance in Ann's direction only to be undone by the sight of Ann crossing her eyes. "Is it too late to get Boyd here?" Ann stage-whispered.

There wasn't time for Lory to second Ann's request. One of the other fire fighters had opened the sliding door and Keith was poised in front of it, ready to jump. Beneath them the fire was crowning through the tall, pitchy timber. Smoke rose hundreds of feet into the air, and the sound of crackling flames battled with the roar of the plane's engine. The path of destruction had already charred hundreds of acres.

Hell, Lory thought. *This is what hell looks like.* Then adrenaline coursed through her, washing away all thoughts, even those of Mike's existence.

"There." Keith pointed. "That's where we'll land. God, would you look at that thing. We've got ourselves an inferno. See ya!" Keith yelled before jumping out.

Next to her, Aaron gasped, but there wasn't time for Lory to see whether the youngster was chickening out. The smoke jumpers had only a few seconds to hurtle themselves into space before the plane was no longer over open ground. Hand on her helmet, Lory counted silently as the rest of the crew followed Keith in quick succession. Aaron had positioned himself so that he would parachute right after Lory, with a seasoned smoke jumper behind him to bring up the tail. "Count," Lory said as she approached the open door. "Don't think. See ya!"

She was free-falling, stomach lurching, laden backpack threatening to throw her off balance. But with years of practice behind her, Lory instinctively went into a spread-eagle arch. She was falling at 120 miles an hour when she reached for the rip cord and put an end to total freedom. Lory had less than a second before Aaron came into view.

He hadn't pulled his rip cord yet. He'd followed her too quickly out of the plane and was tumbling instead of falling stable. "Pull it!" Lory yelled. She gave a yanking motion to emphasize her command.

Aaron yanked on his cord, putting an instant stop to his wild descent. But he'd made a costly error. He was too close to Lory.

When Aaron's larger body slammed into her, there wasn't a thing Lory could do. She was knocked off course without enough time to remedy the situation. Normally that wouldn't have caused a problem, but the meadow was too small, the trees too close.

"Damn!" Lory's oath was lost in the greater sound of her body hitting branches and limbs. Lory ricocheted off the tree she'd crashed into and landed ingloriously on the ground. For a moment only one thought registered.

Mike.

"Lory?" It was Keith. He'd reached her with his parachute still dragging behind him. "You okay?"

She was conscious and able to breathe, so things could have been worse. The parachute tangled around her was an irritant, but at least she wasn't hung up in the tree. "I think so," she tried to reassure Keith. "That wasn't one of my better landings."

"That kid! Who let him loose on us?"

"Don't blame him." Lory was still lying in a crumpled mound, but getting Aaron off the hook seemed more important than trying to pull herself together. "I don't think he'll make that mistake again."

"Can you stand up?"

"It's this blamed parachute," Lory explained. "Give me a minute."

Keith was distracted by the arrival of the other smoke jumpers. Lory took advantage of his back by untangling herself and slowly bringing her feet under her. It wasn't until she'd shucked out of her coveralls and tried to take a step that the throbbing in her right hip registered. Gingerly she touched the spot and winced. Not only was it unbelievably tender, but she could feel blood seeping through her jeans.

"Are you all right? My God, I didn't mean to hit you. I'm sorry."

One look at Aaron's anguished face and Lory made the decision to keep her injury to herself. "I'll live." She gave him a bright smile, being careful not to put any more weight than necessary on her hip. "Don't we have a fire to fight?"

Ten minutes later the crew had stashed their smoke jumping gear and was headed toward the nearest ridge and the monster they'd come here to battle. Although each step threatened to take off the top of Lory's head, she was able to walk. It was only when she stood still for any amount of time that her hip would stiffen up. The blood, she decided, came from a scrape and would stop of its own accord. One thing she was sure of was that she was going to have a beaut of a bruise.

"You're limping," Ann observed.

"I know," Lory admitted. "But that poor kid felt so bad. I just couldn't say anything."

"Are you going to be able to work?"

"I have to," Lory said through taut lips. "The only way we're going to get out of here is after we've licked this thing."

The next five hours passed in a sweaty blur that left Lory little time to think about her injury or the way Mike's name had shot through her in a moment of crisis. Even before Keith's smoke jumpers had arrived, the decision had been made to attack the wildfire by deliberately setting a backfire. Lory wasn't surprised at that extreme measure since the inferno was massive and moving too rapidly through the sunbaked tinderwood to be contained by more conventional fighting methods.

The unpredictability of the wind made the decision a doubly risky one. In order to contain the backfire to the greatest extent possible, the fire fighters first had to clear the ground ahead of where the backfire was going to be set.

Grunts, muttering, heavy breathing and very little conversation surrounded Lory. Like the others, she dug at the earth, slowly exposing the mineral soil beneath. Digging and throwing away the uprooted vegetation worked her shoulders to the point of exhaustion but didn't put any particular strain on her now-swollen hip. The weight of her backpack grew with each hour, and no amount of water from her canteen could quench her thirst. Thoughts of a slowly moving river and hands trailing in the water kept her sane, but the man she'd shared that trip with was only a vague memory. Lory was in a desperate battle to save a forest; she didn't have time to think about herself or the people in her life.

Finally Keith gave the word that it was time to start the backfire and then everyone was to get the hell to the east where, hopefully, the inferno would sweep past them on its collision course with the backfire. Lory watched, fascinated, as Keith sprinted along the line dug by the various crews, deliberately adding to the flames seeking life in the dry summer air. Then, with her boss close at her heels, Lory turned her back and ran for safety.

It was going to work! The efforts of more than fifty fire fighters were going to pay off!

Thoughts of water, ice on her hip, tending to her blisters filled Lory's mind as she and the rest of the hotshot crew stood on a prominence, breathing in smoke as a mountain of flame passed within a half mile of them.

Suddenly Keith's walkie-talkie crackled. He grabbed it but let whoever was on the other end do the talking. When he turned toward his crew, Keith's face was grim. "Wind's shifting. We're in its path."

A few well-chosen curses accompanied Keith's announcement, but none of the fire fighters panicked. "What about the backfire?" someone asked.

"Who knows? Maybe it'll help and maybe it'll add to our problems. We aren't going to have much time. Headquarters says our best chance is if we head south to the rear of the fire."

Lory bit down on her lower lip. The land they would have to cross through was extremely steep, which would slow them to a crawl. That, added to the shape her hip was in, was almost enough to let panic set in.

"What about air support?" Ann asked. "They haven't done any good near as I can see. Can't they get more retardant out here?"

Keith shrugged. "I guess they're putting out calls, but damn it, there are fires everywhere this week. There's only so much that can be done."

Lory understood the position they were in. It was better she knew before Aaron did. The crew had barely picked up their belongings for the retreat when Aaron grabbed Lory's arm. "It's bad, isn't it?" Under sweat and soot, his face was white.

Lory didn't believe in lying. "It can be. It depends on how fast the wind's moving."

"I . . . didn't think it was going to be like this."

"Like what?" Lory asked to keep her mind off what her hip was trying to tell her.

"I don't know." Aaron shrugged before starting to scramble over some rocks. "I was excited. I didn't really think about there being so much noise."

Lory knew what Aaron was talking about. The roar from the fire sounded too much like a train without brakes. That plus the intense heat and flames shooting into the sky would challenge the calmest of nerves. "This is a bad one," Lory tried to explain as she painfully picked her way over the rocks. "It's so dry and the wind—" Concentrating on what she had to make her hip do took away Lory's power of speech.

"I don't want to die."

The words, a child's frightened cry coming from a man's mouth, tore at Lory. They were far enough away from the fire that they were unable to judge its speed, but Lory knew how treacherous the enemy was. In a matter of minutes they could be looking into the face of death. "Don't think that, Aaron. It won't do you any good."

"I can't help it. I've got a girl waiting for me. We're going to get married. I . . . I just want to get back to her."

Lory had been here before. This wasn't the first time the enemy had held the upper hand. In the past she'd thought about her family, the safety of the rest of the crew. This time, however, another element had been added; Aaron's words made that element impossible to ignore.

Lory wanted to get back to Mike.

"You will," she said, wondering whether Aaron would believe her. Wondering whether she did. "You just keep thinking about that girl of yours."

An almost overwhelming wave of loneliness pounded at Lory. Aaron had his girlfriend's love to keep him going. But what did she have? She hadn't told Mike what he'd done to her heart. He hadn't said enough, either.

Maybe she'd never see him again.

Ten minutes later the crew hadn't covered enough ground. The rugged terrain had slowed their retreat to a crawl. Another report from headquarters confirmed what the crew already knew. The fire had made an almost ninety-degree turn and was heading toward them. Across the smoke, Lory locked eyes with Ann. Wordless, the older woman shook her head.

No! The word screamed through Lory. It wasn't supposed to happen like this. Not with so much left undone in her life.

"Lory!"

It couldn't be and yet . . . "Mike?"

"It's me, babe." Static from Keith's walkie-talkie cut off Mike's voice for a moment. "Get yourself into trouble, did you?"

Lory snatched the walkie-talkie from Keith. She was beyond caring who heard what they said to each other. "Where are you?"

"About a mile away from hell. That's a real wall of fire you've got there. How are you doing?"

Lory couldn't tell him about her hip without worrying Keith and scaring Aaron. "It's a little tight. You wouldn't happen to have any marshmallows with you?"

"Sorry. Fresh out. But I've got retardant. And I just got your coordinates. You tell Keith to sit tight. I'm not letting that fire get any closer."

You can do it, my love. "That would be highly appreciated," Lory said in a battle to keep her voice from revealing too much. "We're in a bit of a bind down here."

"I know." The simple words said everything. "It's going to be tight. Sorry."

Tight. Lory's sanity lay in not letting their precarious position overwhelm her. Although she should have turned the walkie-talkie back over to Keith, Lory couldn't force herself to surrender her lifeline. The smoke was too dense to allow her to locate the helicopter; Mike's running commentary kept her aware of everything he was doing. "I can see you," he announced. "Stay together. I'm going to have to drop my load close for it to do any good."

With the drop of Mike's first load of retardant, Lory and the others were given a graphic lesson in Mike's skill. Lory wasn't sure whether she actually heard the helicopter, but it suddenly appeared through the moving mountain of smoke. For a moment it hovered over the exploding energy closest to them. Suddenly red liquid spilled downward, burying flames under its weight.

"Gotta go, babe," Mike said. "But I'll be right back. Tell everyone to stay where they are. I don't want to lose you in this smoke."

No more than five minutes later Mike was back. This time he came even closer to the earth before gently releasing the retardant to the left of his first load. "Damn, I'm good!"

Mike said with a laugh. "Don't go away, kids. I'll be right back."

How many times Mike repeated his message over the next hour, Lory couldn't guess. Time passed at both a maddeningly slow pace and raced at top speed. At Keith's suggestion, the crew turned their energies to the task of drawing a crude line between the rocks and the fire's path. That plus the retardant might stop the forward thrust. Although she worked as hard as those around her, Lory's ears were constantly attuned for Mike's voice.

"We never did get to fish," Mike complained during one drop. "That's what we've got to do the next time we go to the Snake."

"What does your place look like?" he asked the next time he came near. "I've been thinking that maybe it doesn't have electricity or indoor plumbing. Maybe that's why she didn't show it to me."

"Say—" once again Mike's voice gave Lory a pocket of sanity in an insane world "—I never did hear how that arson case turned out. Do you have any idea how much we have to talk about?"

Again: "What's your sister-in-law doing? Did she ever get a job?"

Each time Mike said something that Lory knew was designed to take her mind off the burning wall raging like a wounded animal at the edge of its cage. Each time she tried to give him an answer. She didn't know what the words were, only that talking to Mike was the only thing she needed out of life.

"Listen up, kids. It was a good fight, but I don't think we're going to win," Mike said an hour later. "Tell Keith I think the fire's going to break through to your left."

Wordlessly Lory turned the walkie-talkie over to Keith. She concentrated on digging, trying not to read too much into Keith's expression. "Mike has a better view than we do," Keith told the crew a minute later. "The front's too broad. We're not going to be able to hold it back. I think—" Keith's voice faltered "—we might have to deploy our shelters."

Fear, the first she'd acknowledged today, slammed through Lory. "I don't think I can do it, Keith."

"We don't have any choice. I won't let you panic."

"It isn't that." Keith had handed the walkie-talkie back to Lory, but she was unaware of its weight in her hand. She nodded at Aaron. "That's the one you have to worry about. He's on the raw edge. He might panic. Keith, my hip isn't so hot. I don't think I can lie down."

"What's wrong with your hip?"

Lory jumped at Mike's sharp question. She could have lied to keep him from worrying, but for the past hour her sanity, her life even, had been in his hands. There wasn't anything she couldn't tell him. Quickly she told him about the accident. "If I have to, I will," she finished.

"Brown-and-serve bags."

"What?" Lory asked, distracted by Aaron's restless pacing.

"That's what you called those shelters. I'm not letting any of you wind up in one of them."

"We might not have any choice."

"The hell you won't. I'm getting the woman I love out of there."

Crackling from the walkie-talkie told Lory that Mike was putting distance between himself and the crew. Although she was once more engaged in a frantic scramble to continue the battle, Mike's words were buried deep in her. *I'll get the woman I love out of there.* When Mike made a promise, he kept it.

"Lory?" It was Aaron. "Where'd he go? It's been too long."

Lory didn't want to see the fear in Aaron's eyes, but there was no way she could escape it. "I don't know where he is."

"How are we going to get out of here? Oh, God, I don't want to die!"

Lory threw down her shovel. She didn't know it was going to happen. Her palm was stinging before she realized she'd slapped the young man. "You aren't going to die! Mike won't let any of us die."

"You don't know that." Aaron had backed off from her assault, but at least his eyes were focusing better than they had been a minute ago.

"Yes, I do," Lory said with a conviction that came from her heart. "I know Mike. He . . . won't let anything happen to me."

Aaron stumbled backward and returned to his frantic, futile task. Lory bent over to retrieve her shovel, crying out from the strain she'd put on her hip. Counting was important. She would count every shovelful of dirt she threw back at the fire. *Come, Mike. Now!*

She heard it. After too long without the sound of the helicopter, the powerful engine was once again making an assault on the screaming sound of a forest fire whipped to a frenzy. Before she could look upward, Mike's voice crackled through the walkie-talkie.

"Listen to me," he shouted. "There isn't much time. I've rigged up a sling I think can hold all of you. Get over onto the rocks. I'm going to get as close as I can, but I'm not going to be able to stay down long. The minute the sling hits the ground, I want everyone in it."

"Mike!"

"*Now*, Lory! The wind's picking up steam. We've only got minutes."

Lory was the last to reach the relative safety of the rocks. She wouldn't have made it if Keith hadn't held out his hand to pull her, hip protesting, onto a large boulder. Although

Mike was now directly over them, the sound of the wind-whipped inferno drowned out the chopper's engine. Lory could feel her heart pounding; she just couldn't hear it. The helicopter sank lower, buffeted by the wind. Lory heard Mike's angry curse, but he didn't back off. "Now!" he screamed as the huge canvas net scraped the rocks. "Now!"

He's risking his life. We aren't the only ones in trouble. "Mike, I love you!"

Aaron was the first to scramble onto the sling. Before Lory could wonder at his selfishness, he turned toward her, arms outstretched. "Come on, Lory. You can do it."

On hands and knees, Lory dived for Aaron. Pain made her dizzy, but she fought down the nausea. Around her the other members of the crew were banding together in a tight circle. Lory felt what she thought was the ground shaking under them, but it was Mike pulling the sides of the sling up around them. She fell in a heap against Aaron; this time she didn't try to stifle her moan.

Then they were no longer on the ground. Inch by agonizing inch, Mike lifted the hotshots until they were staring into the center of the fire. The helicopter bucked, attacked by the wind, but Mike fought back. A moment later they were looking down at the ravenous monster. The sling rocked violently as the wind sought to claim Igor, but Lory was, suddenly, without fear.

Mike would take care of her. He couldn't stop the pain in her hip, but he could pull her out of the jaws of death. Tears washed down her cheeks. With the tears went everything Lory had ever known about independence.

She was in Mike's arms. He would keep her safe.

Mike laughed. "That ought to make the six o'clock news."

Lory held the walkie-talkie against her ear, loving the sound of Mike's voice, accepting his relief. "Think you're pretty good, don't you?"

"You're damn right." Mike's voice sobered. "How are you?"

"Fine." *Fine! Wonderful!* "I love you, Mike."

Minutes later Mike was once again maneuvering the helicopter downward. The fire fighters winced as their sling hit the ground. When the canvas sides fell away, they found themselves in the clearing where the fire-fighting operation was centered. Crouching low as protection against the chopper's whirling blades, the crew scrambled off the canvas. Lory struggled to regain her feet, but her hip had been subjected to too much. When Aaron leaned over, she fastened her arms around his neck and let him carry her.

"Gotta go now, babe," Mike was telling her. "I better make sure no one else is in trouble."

Lory held on to Aaron until he'd carried her to a grassy spot. Once on the ground, she buried her fingers in the cool dirt. Keith dropped to his knees beside her. His white face mirrored what she knew she looked like. "I don't ever want to do that again," he said fervently.

"Neither do I." How long had it been since Mike had come on the scene? All she knew, all she cared about, was that her existence had been fundamentally changed today. Before Mike her independence had been at the center. It had formed the core of her self-confidence, her pride in what she did for a living.

But Mike had taught her something essential about dependence. He'd said he wouldn't let anything happen to her; she believed him.

His actions justified her trust.

Although it was late afternoon, Keith and the rest of his hotshot team made the decision to lend support to the crews working the fire's left flank. Lory watched them leave, envying them because they could use activity to stem the emotional impact of what they'd just gone through. Lory was left with little except her exhausted, hurting body and emotions that cut deeper than anything had ever cut before.

She loved Mike. Completely. Utterly. Despite the joy she felt, the depth and breadth of her love was a frightening thing. What if Mike didn't return the emotion?

He has other work to do, Lory told herself. That's why he isn't here now. She believed her words. What she couldn't quite believe was that when he returned there would no longer be distance between them. She had no skills for attacking the wall of independence surrounding Mike.

If that hadn't been stripped from him as it had been from her, then she would be forced to tell him goodbye—one final time.

Mike wasn't the only helicopter pilot fighting the fire, but he was the last one to give up the day's battle. Most of the crew had come dragging into camp by the time Lory saw the great silver machine settle to earth. When Mike emerged from the cockpit, Lory forced herself to her feet and took the first tentative steps. After a half-dozen feet, she had to stop. She was breathing heavily to still the pounding in her hip when Mike reached her.

His arms were open and inviting. Nothing mattered except losing herself in the waiting haven. *Hold me, Mike. Don't ever let me go!* "Hi," she whispered against his chest.

"Hi yourself."

Lory didn't recognize Mike's voice. She tried to tell herself that the day's efforts had changed it, but today had been for putting an end to all lies, all deception. "What's wrong?"

"Nothing's wrong." Mike held her against him, his arms tight and possessive until Lory almost believed him. Then he thrust her away from him, his fingers digging into her arms. She really was alive! That's what he wanted to think about, not what was tearing at his gut. "You look like hell."

Lory had tried to wash the dirt, sweat and dried tears from her face, but she knew the day was still etched on her. "I can't help it."

Yes, she could. She didn't have to do this to herself. To either of them. "God, I hate your job!"

Nothing else he could have said could have wounded Lory as much as that. "Don't . . . say that."

"Why?" What churned in Mike's gut forced the question. "Can't you handle the truth?"

"Don't talk to me about truth." Love and exhaustion and pain and needing allowed Lory to strip her soul bare. "That's the only thing I have thought about today."

"And what have you learned?"

"That I could have never made it without you. You saved my life, Mike."

"Did I?" The remnants of fear had turned Mike into someone he didn't recognize. He needed time to think, but time was a luxury he didn't have. "Or maybe I just postponed the inevitable."

"What are you talking about?"

"About this damn job of yours killing you someday." Lory expected to have Mike turn away, to leave her drowning. Instead he pulled her back against him and branded her raw lips with a violent kiss. "Walk away from it, Lory. For me, walk away from it!"

This wasn't what she wanted, what she needed. Nothing was going right. "I'd never ask you to give up your job."

"It isn't the same thing. Look at yourself, Lory. You can hardly stand up. Your eyes look... Think about where you'd be right now if it wasn't for me."

"I'd be crawling out from under my shelter." Lory had forgotten how to move her lips. "I wouldn't be dead."

"You don't know that. You could have died today."

"What would you have done then? Blamed me?" That wasn't what she wanted to say, but it was too late to take back the words.

"Maybe. Walk away from it, Lory. While you still can."

"Don't tell me how to run my life." Lory had placed her life in his hands earlier today and known it was right. But that was earlier. Now he was ordering her and she wouldn't be ordered. "I won't have it."

Mike's hands slid away, releasing Lory, forcing her to stand alone. He'd lied when he'd told her she looked like hell. Yes, her eyes were red-rimmed, her cheeks rubbed raw from heat and wind. She stood awkwardly with her weight resting on her good hip. But she was still the most beautiful woman Mike had ever known. Making love to her had been the most exquisite experience of his life. She belonged in his arms; he'd do anything to make that happen again.

Or would he? This strong, vulnerable woman was attacking everything Mike Steen had ever believed about himself. Loner, people called him. Until Lory had entered his life, Mike had accepted that as the truth. Even when she'd begun her gentle assault on his heart, he'd fought. Together and apart. Together and apart. That had been the tempo of their relationship.

It had satisfied him.

The hell it had. If it had, he wouldn't be here now.

Mike Steen was scared. His fear had nothing to do with what he'd battled while trying to get Lory out of the woods alive. He was face-to-face with emotions he'd never faced before, a caring he'd never felt before.

"You're right, Lory," he said through everything that was swirling around him. "I won't ever try to tell you what to do. You don't need me. Hell, you don't need anyone."

Mike was wrong. Terribly wrong. Finally nothing was left but words of truth. "I needed Jeff."

Mike acknowledged the still faintly beating fear of giving too much of himself. Anger too was in there somewhere. But both those emotions were being shoved aside. In their wake was an almost overwhelming need to protect Lory. Not from losing Jeff, but from what he'd just said. Lory had been through enough today, and yet he was putting her through even more. He should be holding her, telling her that he would always be there to keep her safe, that he was the one to take Jeff's place.

But Lory Foster wasn't weak or helpless. She'd been battling raging demons for three years. She would go on doing that or stop being the woman he'd fallen in love with. "Did you happen to ask yourself what I was doing here today?"

"What?" Lory clamped down on her lip, stopping its trembling. "Why are you here?"

"Because I knew that's where you were."

Mike was trying to tell her something, but Lory could only guess at what that something was. She'd been steeling herself to have him walk out of her life—surely she'd given him reason to—but he was still here. The need for honesty that had propelled her this far gave her the strength to take the next step. "Was that important to you?"

"Yes."

"Why?"

"It wasn't because I thought I was going to wind up bailing you out."

"Why then?"

"Because..." Mike held out his hand, keeping it outstretched even when Lory didn't take it. "Because I had to see you. Because I shouldn't have let you go the last time."

Lory felt her hip start to buckle under her. In the process of regaining her balance she found Mike's hand. "Are you sure?"

"Yes, I'm sure." Mike took the step that erased the distance between them. Once again his arms were around her.

This time he gave her nothing except tenderness. "I love you, Lory."

"Love?"

"I said it before. I'm still saying it," Mike whispered. When Lory started to open her mouth, he covered her lips with his. This kiss was a world apart from the earlier cruel assault.

He loved her. There had been so many things she'd wanted to tell Mike, so much that needed to be said. They needed to talk about the forces in them that made them what they were and couldn't be changed. But that could come later.

He loved her.

Chapter Thirteen

Lory was grateful for the peanut butter and jelly sandwiches that distracted the crew from asking about her hip.
Although there was the usual grumbling, the fire fighters
were hungry enough to tackle anything, even a quickly as-
sembled meal brought in by one of the last planes to land
before dark. Whether she got anything to eat meant little to
Lory. What mattered was that she and Mike were alone.

"It's the best I could find," Mike explained as he handed
Lory a small ice pack. "If nothing else, it should numb your
hip."

Without removing her jeans, Lory laid the pack gently
against her hip. A minute later she sighed in relief. "Better.
I'm not sure I want to see what it looks like."

"Neither do I." Mike dropped to his knees and joined
Lory on the tarp he'd lifted from someone's bedding. For a
minute they listened to the distant murmur of voices. "It's
been an incredible day," he said finally.

"It has. The fire—that's as close as I ever want to get to
something that unstoppable." Lory shook her head. She
didn't want to talk about the fire. Not yet. She concentrated on the courage she needed to ask her question. "Did
you really mean what you said?"

"I said a lot of things today, Lory." Although Mike was sitting only a few inches away, he hadn't tried to touch her. His eyes were on the activity down the hill from them.

"I know. The things you said while you were in the air, they kept me sane." With her free hand, Lory reached for Mike's arm. He let her touch him but didn't return the contact. "Did you mean it about why you came here? It wasn't because you thought I might be in trouble?"

"No. Maybe, considering the way it turned out, I should have, but I've always known you were competent."

Lory indicated her hip. "I don't feel very competent tonight."

"You couldn't help that. I'm serious. You're well trained. We both are."

"Maybe." She could have continued to skirt around what really needed to be said, but their being together was precious. After what they'd gone through today, she wasn't going to risk losing the magic by talking of everyday things. "Professionally we are, but, Mike, we haven't been handling things very well personally."

Mike didn't speak. His eyes still hadn't met hers. Taking strength from the emotions swirling around her, Lory forced herself to continue. "You said you shouldn't have let me go the last time. Why?"

"Didn't I make that clear?"

"You . . ." This was so hard. She'd never been down this road before. "You said you loved me."

Once again Mike slid into silence. Although he nodded, the gesture wasn't nearly enough. "Are you sorry you said that?" Lory asked. She wasn't able to get her voice above a whisper.

"No. Never."

He still wasn't giving her enough of what was going on inside him. But maybe it was because she hadn't given him anything except three words without enough surrounding them. It wasn't going to be like that anymore. "It was bad today, Mike," she said. "As bad as anything I've ever been through. Maybe we could have crawled into our shelters and come out of it alive, but . . ." Lory shuddered. "That's the kind of experience nightmares are made of. But you said you'd get us out of there. I believed you." Her lips started trembling again, not from fear, but from the impact of what she was about to say. "I knew it was going to be all right."

"It was close, Lory."

"I know that." Once again she took a chance on touching his arm. Energy and something more entered her. "I'm not trying to put you on a white charger. That wouldn't be fair. But I heard your voice. I knew you wouldn't let anything happen to me."

Lory had started to withdraw her hand, but Mike covered it with his, holding her fingers against his strong forearm. "It's going to happen again."

"What is?"

"You risking your life."

"You, too," Lory pointed out. "You almost lost it trying to get us out. Don't tell me you didn't."

"It was worth the risk."

Lory rested her tired body against the strong one next to her. They both smelled of smoke and their stomachs were rumbling. She hurt too much for anything more than a gentle caress, but incredible things were happening tonight. She could only pray that what they felt was strong enough to allow her to ask her next question. "Do you really hate my job?"

Turning his body so he could look into Lory's eyes, Mike held her face in his hands. "I did say that, didn't I?"

"Yes, you did." Maybe he was waiting for her to make the move that would end in yet another kiss, but there were still things they had to say before she could lose herself in him.

Mike sighed. "I won't deny that. Lory, I was mad and scared. I almost lost you today. It could have gone that way. We both know it. But . . . no, I don't hate your job."

"You don't? You scared me." There was too much relief in Lory's voice, but she couldn't hold back.

"What I hated, what I will probably always hate, are the risks you take for your job. But, Lory, sweetheart, I'd never ask you to give it up. You wouldn't be the same person without it."

He understood! Tonight Lory might want to break her shovel over the nearest rock and turn her back on the past three years of her life. But the feeling wouldn't last. By morning she would be ready to attack the inferno again. And the beautiful thing was, Mike knew that. "You scared me," she admitted. "I really believed you."

"I meant it when I said the words." Although he was still holding her face, continuing the eye contact, Mike leaned back a few inches. He was studying more than the surface. "And I might say the same thing again. But, Lory, I love who you are, not what I might want you to become."

"And I love you, Mike. I think I've loved you since we were on the Snake."

Mike took a deep breath. "You, too? I remember being scared. You were doing things to me I'd never experienced before. I didn't know how to handle what I was feeling."

"I know," Lory admitted with new wisdom. "That's why I didn't ask when I'd see you again. I wasn't used to needing anyone the way I need you. I was scared. I'm not anymore."

He kissed her then, a gentle union born of respect, admiration and honesty. The ice pack slipped from Lory's hand and dropped to the tarp as she slid her arms around his neck. Earlier today Mike had been no more than a vibrant voice on a walkie-talkie. That voice had been her lifeline; he'd had nothing more to give her then. But it wasn't enough now. She needed his warmth, his strength, his presence, to survive and grow.

"I think...I think it's a good thing there isn't any privacy here," Mike said when the kiss ended.

"We could go into the forest."

"Not tonight, love." Mike laughed. The sound washed over what his kiss had done to her nerve endings, bringing her even more to life than she'd been a moment ago. "Not with your hip the way it is."

"I don't care. All right." Lory made herself match his light mood. "But tomorrow..."

"What am I going to do with you, woman?" Mike nipped at her lips. "Not only do I have to put up with your crazy job, but you're going to turn me into a tired old man before my time."

"Oh—" Lory ran her finger down the bridge of Mike's nose "—I think you're equal to the task. I just wish..."

"Don't stop now. Anything you want to say, say it."

"It's not about us," Lory explained. "I was wondering if Jeff and his fiancée ever talked the way we are."

Mike returned the gesture by gently putting a forefinger on Lory's closed lips. "Do you think it would have made a difference?"

"I think so. I didn't tell you everything about the night Jeff was killed." Lory waited for the familiar wave of sorrow to engulf her. When it came, Mike was there to shield her against it. "Carrie didn't want him to fight fires anymore. Jeff never could make her understand how much it meant to him. They argued. She gave him back his ring. Jeff told me something I've never forgotten." Lory paused, reading in Mike's eyes his willingness to listen. "He said he didn't think he and Carrie loved each other enough. If they had, they would have respected each other's needs more. She would have understood that what he did was more than just a job. And just before he walked away Jeff told me that if he had loved Carrie enough, maybe he could have listened to her fears."

Instead of saying anything, Mike once again pulled Lory into the circle of his warmth. It was incredible. A few minutes ago he'd been angry enough to shake her. Now the final barriers were falling away. It wasn't anger he'd felt, after all, but an overwhelming need for honesty. He was sorry for Jeff and Carrie. If they'd been as honest as he and Lory were, maybe Jeff wouldn't have died that night.

He and Lory couldn't change the past. There was only tonight. And tomorrow. "That's why I'm here. I flew here because I had to tell you how I feel. To hope to hear you say the same thing."

"Did you know I loved you?" Lory was shaking; she couldn't help it.

With a kiss, Mike stilled her trembling. "I'm not that intuitive, sweetheart. I haven't wanted to be intuitive before you. But what I felt was strong enough to be worth taking a chance."

"A chance?" Lory repeated. A minute ago she'd been forging new paths through their relationship. Now that she'd faltered, he was picking up the slack.

"I need to tell you something," Mike whispered. "That day at my mother's school I thought about how Jeff's death must have affected you. I told myself that maybe you weren't able to risk giving and losing like that again." Mike put his hand over her mouth to stop her. "That's why—once again—I made myself tell you goodbye."

"That's not—"

"Don't," Mike stopped her once more. "I need to finish. I know. That was crazy thinking, but then you do crazy things to me, sweetheart. I said I was here today because I needed to tell you how I feel. That's only part of it. What I want is to ask you to take a chance on another relationship, one that will go places your friendship with Jeff never went."

"I don't want a relationship, Mike."

"You—"

"That isn't enough. A relationship is something that happens now. It doesn't say anything about the future."

"I thought you understood that's what I wanted. A future, I mean. Lory." Mike placed a kiss on her eyelids. "You're the only future I want or need. I need to know you're always going to be there."

"Marriage?" Lory asked. "Are you talking about getting married?"

"Are you proposing?"

"Yes." Love gave Lory the courage to face Mike. "I am."

"Then I accept."

AT DAWN MIKE HELPED Lory into the Sikorsky and brought the machine to life. As they rose above the ground, they could see the fire fighters lining up to replace those who'd fought the fire during the night. Lory longed to be with them, but until her hip healed she would only be a hindrance. Mike, however, was needed.

Mike explained where he would be flying for water to mix with retardant and pointed out that Lory was along to keep him company, not to tell him how to do his job. After having spent the night nestled against her new fiancé's side, Lory was secure. She warmed to his easy teasing. "You know," she said as the inferno came into view, "there's something I'm going to insist we do as soon as this fire is out."

"Is it going to cost me a lot of money?"

Lory had never seen a fire quite this way before. It was incredibly close and yet removed from what she was experiencing. "I want to see where you live. Take me there, Mike. Please."

"I'd rather see your place. Yours is a home. Mine has always been where I hang my hat."

"That can change. We can make yours into a home. Mike? I've been thinking. I'd rather live close to your mother than my family. I don't like the idea of her being alone."

"Are you sure? You grew up around the Snake."

Lory hung on as Mike made a sharp right turn and headed toward a small lake. "The Snake will always be there. And as long as we have Igor, it won't take long to get there. I've watched you and your mother together. I don't want to take you away from her."

Mike's hands and feet continued to do their job. His mind, however, was a million miles away from what he was being paid to do. "You're a good woman, Lory."

The glow that had burned within Lory since yesterday became even stronger. "It's not me, Mike. She's an easy woman to love. Besides, someone has to water her garden once she retires and starts going on those trips you told me about."

"They're summer trips, Lory. You know what our summers are like."

Mike was right. Her summers, before he entered her life, had been insanity. But excitement and challenge, and yes, danger, no longer filled her the way they always had. Something—someone had come along to change that. "They won't always be like that," she told him. "I love what I do. I probably always will. But, Mike, there's more to life than fighting fires. Things I haven't dared think about before now."

"What kind of things, honey?"

Honey. If he could call her that, she could tell him what was in her heart. "Mike, I want children." Lory swallowed. "I need to hold my own baby. Our baby." She looked at him, took courage from what was in his eyes and went on. "Boyd and Sal, they're changing their lives for their baby. When our time comes, I want to do the same."

"Children. When?"

Lory stared at her hands. Until she said the words, she had no idea how much motherhood meant to her. Now she knew—having Mike's baby would make her whole. "When we're ready."

"A baby. I used to think I'd never... That has to be more your decision than mine, honey," Mike was telling her. His eyes were saying he'd been touched as deeply as she had. "I don't care what they say about mixing motherhood and a career. Certain careers, yes, but not one that takes you God knows where for months at a time."

"I know," Lory said softly. In the saying, she made the most important decision of her life—next to asking Mike to marry her. "I feel the same way."

"No regrets? It won't bother you to give up fire fighting?"

"I can't say there won't be some regrets." His eyes asked for so much honesty from her. Good. She was ready to give him that. "A piece of me will always want to be fighting fires. It's something I'm proud to be doing. But being a wife and mother—that's more important."

"I want you to do whatever makes you happy, Lory. There's only one thing I don't think I could handle and that's wondering if the mother of my child is going to make it home alive. Please don't do that to us."

"I won't," Lory whispered. For a moment words caught in her throat and then she went on. "I can teach fire-fighting techniques. And the investigations—I've always wanted more time for that."

"Children." Wonder transformed Mike's voice. "I think we'd be good at it. But not too soon. We need time for us. There's so many things I want to share with you. I was thinking... I hope you have time off this coming winter."

"I might." Although she might be risking their safety, Lory ran her hand down Mike's arm. He responded with a smile that went to her heart. "What did you have in mind?" she asked him.

"Showing you things that mean a lot to me. Letting you see the things that helped form me. Have you ever flown over Montana in the fall?"

"I don't think so."

"You would have remembered." Mike smiled again. "When the mountain aspens turn color, there's nothing like it. The sense of the changing seasons—I want you to see more of the world from where I see it. People who spend their lives on the ground miss a lot."

"Oh, they do, do they?" There was smoke but no fire where they were now. During the night the wind had quieted. Maybe the battle would be won today. Maybe they could, for a few days, lay down the responsibilities that had brought them together. Lory wanted that, almost desperately. Like him, there was so much of her world she wanted to introduce him to. "You can't see elk from the air. Really see them. How would you like to watch a newborn elk calf take its first steps? There's a herd not far from where I live. They've gotten used to having me around."

"A newborn elk calf? You've really seen one?" At Lory's nod Mike went on. "Did I tell you that I'm one hell of a photographer? Mostly aerial, but I'd love to try something new. That's something we could do together." Mike's eyes lingered on Lory. "One of the things we can do together." It wasn't until the helicopter continued to climb that she realized he was still looking at her.

"Mike," she warned.

Mike brought the helicopter back under control. A few seconds later the trees broke away and they were over the high mountain lake that had been Mike's lifeline yesterday. Lory watched, fascinated, as Mike expertly maneuvered the helicopter lower until the canvas sling underneath sank into the lake. When they rose, the sling was full. "Nothing to it," Mike boasted. "Wait till you see me haul a tree out of the woods. That's really something to see."

"Hmm." Lory wasn't sure whether she was still smiling or the warm emotion she felt was only in her heart. "I see I've gotten myself hooked up with a modest man."

"You really feel that way? Hooked up, I mean."

"Hooked up in the most wonderful way imaginable. I love you," Lory whispered.

"Forever?"

"Yes, forever."

Mike sighed. The sound took Lory's attention away from what was going on around them. This was their world, but what was taking place between them was more important. "Do you have any idea how that makes me feel?" Mike asked. Before Lory could attempt an answer, he went on. "Good. Wonderful. Excited and scared. I didn't think it would ever be like that. I've never been emotionally dependent on anyone before. Especially not someone as competent as you are."

Lory understood what Mike meant by scared. An emotion as overwhelming as love was more earth-shattering than any forest fire. At least they were experiencing it together. "Competent? Is that what you think I am?"

"That's what I know." The look Mike gave her was one of pure love. And the promise of tonight. "The mistake I made was confusing competence with not needing," he was telling her. "I used to think I didn't need anyone. I thought I'd met a woman just like me. Neither of us needed anything or anyone."

"No," Lory whispered. In a few seconds Mike would be too busy to listen to her. She had to say it now. "I was never like that. I needed Jeff. I need you more. In different ways."

"In what ways, sweetheart?"

Lory focused on Mike's strong hands on the controls. The morning sun streamed through the Plexiglas and danced in his eyes. Under her, Igor rocked. How many mornings, she wondered, would she and Mike spend like this? A hundred? A thousand? They wouldn't always be fighting fires. Sometimes they'd be flying to the Snake or hovering over the forest seeking a quick view of a newborn elk. And sometimes there would be no more reason for seeking the sky than a wealth of emotion that needed to escape the confines of earth.

"In every way," she told him without reservation. "For the rest of my life."

The rest of their life began that day. Although, except for refueling stops, they remained in the helicopter until almost dark, their thoughts and words went far beyond the confining space or the angry, surrendering monster below them. A small, family-oriented wedding was planned, a honeymoon to the Southern California seashore sketched.

Lory had occasionally wondered what it would feel like to plan her wedding. She learned that the details meant little. She would get a dress—what it looked like didn't matter as long as Mike liked it. The only thing she cared about was that they be married out-of-doors. "There's a fine line between the end of the fire season and when it gets too cold in our neck of the woods. I hope we've picked the right date."

Mike wasn't concerned. It wouldn't matter if it rained on their wedding day. The woman sitting next to him was sunlight and life. He could no longer remember what it felt like to sit alone in this world he'd created for himself. Mike didn't believe in comparing himself to others. They had employers; he ran his own show. They had families waiting for them at the end of a workday; until now he hadn't asked himself if he'd wanted to be anything but alone.

Now it was different. Now he had Lory. And in her touch and eyes he had everything.

"It's a wrap," he told her when the sun was no longer strong enough to invade their privacy. "They're not going to need me tomorrow. Where do you want to spend the night?"

Lory remembered the first time he'd asked her that. Back then she'd insisted on separate rooms and accepted their separate lives. Everything had changed. "With you," she whispered. Her eyes ached from staring down through the trees. Her legs tingled with the need to move. "Anywhere as long as we're together."

Mike banked the helicopter and left the fire behind. "It won't be fancy."

"Does it have a bed?"

Mike nodded.

"Can anyone reach us there?"

"No."

"Then it has everything we need."